LANDMARK COLLECTOR'S LIBRARY

Stationary Steam Engines of Great Britain

The National Photographic Collection

Volume 7: The South and South West

Cornwall, Devon, Dorset, Hampshire, Isle of Wight, Somerset & Wiltshire

George Watkins

The Watkins Collection in the National Monuments Record

This comprises the photographs and notes George Watkins made during a lifetime of study of the stationary steam engine.

The Steam Engine Record is an annotated set of around 1500 mounted prints of steam engines (and thousands of others) which Watkins examined in the field between 1930 and 1980. His notebooks contain a record of additional sites for which no photographs were taken, or which comprise written historical notes. In all almost 2000 entries were made in his notebooks. There are also albums of prints arranged by engine type. A catalogue is available.

In addition there are files of notes and other records on all aspects of historical steam technology, the cataloguing of which is in progress.

The main areas of this part of the collection are:

Records of steam engine makers.

Collection of bound trade literature.

Classified collection of data files dealing with, for example, textile mill engines, marine engines.

The collection can be inspected by appointment. Copies of photographs and other documents are readily available.

Please contact:

NMR Enquiry & Research Services
National Monuments Record Centre
Kemble Drive
Swindon
Wilts
SN2 2GZ

STATIONARY STEAM ENGINES OF GREAT BRITAIN

THE NATIONAL PHOTOGRAPHIC COLLECTION

VOLUME 7: THE SOUTH AND SOUTH WEST
Cornwall, Devon, Dorset, Hampshire, Isle of Wight, Somerset & Wiltshire

George Watkins

Landmark Publishing

Published by

LANDMARK
Publishing Ltd

Ashbourne Hall, Cokayne Ave
Ashbourne, Derbyshire, DE6 1EJ England
Tel: (01335) 347349 Fax: (01335) 347303
e-mail: landmark@clara.net
web site: www.landmarkpublishing.co.uk

ISBN 1 901522 88 1

Print: Bookcraft, Midsomer Norton, Bath
Designed by: James Allsopp
Editor: A P Woolrich
Production: C L M Porter

Front cover: SER 1373A
Back cover: SER 232
Page 3: SER 1207

CONTENTS

FOREWORD
by A. P. Woolrich

George Watkins (1904-1989) spent most of his working life as a heating engineer and boilerman in Bristol. Starting in the 1930s, in his spare time he made short trips throughout Britain photographing and recording stationary steam engines. In 1965, aged 61, he was appointed a research assistant at the Centre for the Study of the History of Technology at Bath University, under Dr R. A. Buchanan, and was enabled to devote all his time adding to and classifying his collection. He was still making field trips until the late 1970s, when ill-health made travelling difficult.

He was an occasional contributor to *Model Engineer* and other periodicals, and wrote important papers for the *Transactions of the Newcomen Society*. Following his appointment to Bath University he was in much demand as a lecturer and produced a series of books based on his research. These were:

The Stationary Steam Engine (1968)

The Textile Mill Engine, 2 Vol, (1970, 1971), 2ed, (1999)

Man and the Steam Engine, (1975), 2 imp (1978) (with R. A. Buchanan)

The Industrial Archaeology of the Stationary Steam Engine, (1976) (with R. A. Buchanan)

The Steam Engine in Industry 2 vol, (1978, 1979)

On his death in February 1989 his collection was gifted to the Royal Com-mission on the Historical Monuments of England. It may be freely consulted at English Heritage's National Record Centre at Swindon. As well as photographs the collection comprises numerous technical notes about all manner of steam engine related topics; an incomparable archive of trade catalogues, some dating from the late nineteenth century; a collection of letters from like-minded friends, of value today for the light they shed on the history of the growth of Industrial Archaeology; lecture notes and slides. His library was left to Bath University.

He would visit a site and take illustrated notes and photographs, usually around half a dozen. His notes usually contained measured sketches of the machines and also the layouts of the premises he visited. In all, he travelled over 120,000 miles and visited nearly 2,000 sites, but in approximately 10% only took written notes. He filed sets of contact prints of each visit in binders sorted by engine type and between 1965-1971 he made a selection of the best prints for Bath University staff to print to a larger format. These were drymounted on card and annotated with details from his field notebooks and today form what is known at the Steam Engine Record. It is this collection, with notes, which forms the basis of the present series of regional books.

The Steam Engine Record is filed in numerical order, but catalogues are available listing makers, engine types and locations. When the field trips were being made the historic county names still applied, but the modern catalogues in the Search Room at Swindon allow searching by new counties and metropolitan areas, such as Cleveland and Greater Manchester. In this series, however, the historical county names have been retained.

When he began his surveys, he travelled by bicycle and train, and many were to sites he could reach readily from Bristol, but he soon graduated to a series of autocycles, on which he would pack his photographic gear and his clothing. He planned his trips meticulously during the winter months, writing to mill owners to gain permission, and then during following summer (when his boiler was shut down for maintenance), having saved up all his available leave time, would then spend two or three weeks on his travels, staying in bed-and-breakfast accommodation, or, as he became more widely known, with friends. During the autumn he would write up his notes, and begin planning the following year's trip.

He was initially interested in beam engines, but soon concentrated on the textile mill engines of mostly Lancashire and Yorkshire. In this he was greatly aided by local experts such as Frank Wightman and Arthur Roberts, who were working in these areas. Later his interest included colliery winding engines, waterworks and marine engines. During the War, when he found difficulty in both travelling far and in getting permission to enter industrial sites, he investigated water-powered sites, such as the Avon Valley brass mills, near Bristol, and the Worcestershire edge tool manufacturing sites. An area of steam technology which did not concern him was the railway locomotive, though he did record a small number of industrial locomotives and traction engines he found on his visits.

The regional distribution of the sites he visited includes most English counties and a number in Wales and Scotland. The numbers of sites he saw in the counties differ greatly, with Yorkshire, Lancashire, and the counties around Bristol predominating. This is because he had close links with other workers in those areas, and he relied on this network to learn where engines might be found. Areas where he had few contacts tended to be thinly covered.

In many counties he saw sites with a marine connection. These will be covered in Volume 10 of this series. In this context this means a steam engine which drove a vessel, whether at sea, river or canal; also preserved marine engines. Engines at waterside features such as dockside workshops are included in the regional sequence of books.

George Watkins often photographed under near impossible conditions. Engine-room lighting was frequently indifferent, and confined space often made hard the siting of the camera for obtaining adequate perspective views. For most of the work reproduced in this series he used a tripod-mounted wooden plate camera with extension bellows which he modified to accept different lenses. In his early years he was continually experimenting with different combinations of film speeds, lenses and exposure times. Although he did eventually own a 35mm roll film camera, he was never happy with using it, and was frequently heard to grumble about the quality of modern film stock.

He used cut film, held in a dark slide, and had the films developed by a local chemist in the centres he visited so he could go back and take another if a print failed. He overcame bad lighting by having very long exposures, so was able to appear in his own prints occasionally.

The long exposures also meant he was able to 'freeze' a slow-moving engine. He did this by shielding the lens by a hand-held card or the lens cap until the engine had reached, say, top dead centre and then removing the shield momentarily. This cumulative exposure resulted in an image of a still engine, and such was his deftness of touch and impeccable timing, that it is very hard to see any kind of shake or blemish on the photographs. He was adept at 'painting with light' - utilising hand-held electric lead-lights with which he could illuminate different parts of the engine successively.

He made copies from his negatives at home for distribution to his friends by using a simple contact-print frame and developer chemicals. There are many small sets of his prints in private hands.

The lenses he used were not bloomed to prevent 'flaring' of the image caused by extraneous light from windows or hanging light bulbs, and some of the photographs reproduced are marred by this. He made his selection of prints for the Steam Engine Record on the basis of their historical and technical importance, and not on their artistic quality.

His photographs are a unique record of the end of stationary steam power in this country, being made at a time when electrification, nationalisation and trade depression created wholesale changes in the physical structure of the industrial landscape. They are an invaluable re-source to our understanding of the reality of industrial activity, and will interest, as well as the technical histo-rian, the local historian and model-maker. It is good to know they are being published, for this in turn will focus attention on the rest of his re-ference collection, which deserves to be more widely known and used.

ISSES (The International Stationary Steam Engine Society) is publishing a number of volumes devoted to George Watkins and his work. The first volume was published mid-2002. It includes a biography of George Watkins, reminis-cences by his friends, and copies of a number of his earlier writings, includ-ing some unpublished ones from the 1930's, and an account of the Watkins collection at Swindon,

Details and prices may be obtained from:

Mr John Cooper,
73 Coniston Way, Blossom Hill,
Bewdley, Worcestershire,
DY12 2QA
Tel: 01299 402946

Email:
John.Cooper@isses2.freeserve.co.uk
Web site: www.steamenginesociety.org

The sites are in alphabetical order of geographical location, and then site name and no attempt has been made to place them by precise grid references. As work on this series has progressed it has become plain that the locations are sometimes wrong, particularly county names. This is because George used the nearest post town, which was some-times in the next county. This has caused problems when allocating the entries to the books of this regional se-ries, so work has been done closely cross checking the remaining original SER cards and revising the headings as nec-essary.

Each entry heading has an illustration number for this volume, the location, revised as necessary and the Steam Engine Record (SER) number. This lat-ter number is the key for accessing the copies of the field notebooks and the files of additional photographs in the National Monuments Record at Swindon.

The remaining pages of this intro-duction comprise brief illustrated notes to explain detail and a glossary of some of the terms he uses.

CORNWALL

Only one site was visited in Cornwall. The reason for this is that when George Watkins started his travels in the 1930s, the Cornish Engines Preservation Society (now the Trevithick Society) was engaged on a photographic survey of surviving engines in the county, and he did not wish to repeat their work. Although this survey was completed, it has never been formally published.

Towards the end of his life he was much engaged in consultancy work on the engines at the Wendron Forge project, but he did not photograph any of the work done there.

DEVON

Only two sites were seen in Devon, one a textile mill and the other a set of rare mine stamps which had been working in the 1960s.

DORSET

Sites visited in the county included those relating to brewing, water supply and sewage treatment, a pottery and a sawmill.

HAMPSHIRE

In Hampshire he saw engines used in contracting, water supply, brewing and a gas works.

ISLE OF WIGHT

Only two sites were visited on the island.

SOMERSET

The bulk of the sites included in this book were in Somerset. In the 1930s he made a very important survey of the steam pumps used to drain the Somerset Levels, and though he wrote it up at the time, it was not published until after his death. During World War II, when he had difficulties getting into industrial plant he made a photographic survey and collected information from surviving workers about the brass making sites along the Avon Valley at Keynsham and Saltford.

In the Bridgwater area he photographed a very early beam engine on the Bridgwater and Taunton Canal, and a rare design of a traversing bridge over the River Parrett. In the Bath area he photographed engines in a gas works, textile and paper mills, and early water-powered pumps at Claverton used to maintain the water level of the Kennet and Avon Canal.

Several water works pumping engines owned by the Bristol Water-works Co were surveyed in the north of the county and other waterworks engines were seen at Bridgwater, Frome, and Weston-super-Mare.

Textile mills with steam engines were seen at Chard, Glastonbury and Taunton.

WILTSHIRE

Sites visited include a brewery, an ironworks, a gas works, and the steam pumps at Crofton used to maintain the levels of the Kennet and Avon Canal.

FURTHER READING

George Watkins, 'Steam engine drainage of the Somerset Levels', in Paul Stephens and Tony Woolrich, eds., *George Middleton Watkins 1904-1989*, vol 1, (2002), pp 65-78.

Beam engine, the original form as made by Boulton and Watt. This form owed its existence to the fact that all the earlier steam engines were used for pumping water, the beam forming a convenient means of attachment for the pump rods.

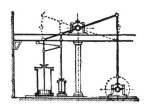

Horizontal Engine, with open frame cast iron bedplate, a type much used for all sizes of engine for general purposes. The bed-plate frame was of a U section, and was bolted down to a foundation of masonry or brickwork, the cylinder, main bearing and guides being bolted to the bed-plate.

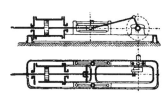

Vertical engine, a type used extensively for both large and small engines; it had the advantage of occupying little floor space. An endless number of varieties of this type was developed, and it was the generally accepted type for marine screw-propeller engines.

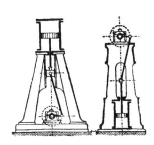

Corliss frame or Girder Engine, a type of horizontal engine. This example had a bored guide, but they were also made with flat-planed guides. In both cases the guides were formed in the main casting or girder which connects the cylinder to the main bearing. There were many varieties of this type.

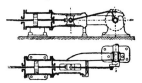

Self contained horizontal engines, with bent or slotted out cranks. This type, largely used for small power short-stroke engines had the cylinder bolted on to the end of an open bedplate, which was widened out at the other end to take both bearings of the crank shaft, so that the flywheel might be keyed on either side. The guides were usually formed in the bedplate, the boring out of the guides and facing of the end flange being done at the same setting.

Oscillating Engines, formerly much used as marine engines. Originally developed for driving paddle wheels, this type has also been used for driving screw propellers. Uncommon in land use.

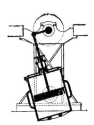

Steeple engine, formerly used for driving paddle wheels. A variety of this type had been used for small powers, and was known as the Table Engine.

Beam Engine, Woolf's Compound. Two unequal cylinders side by side, at one end of the beam. Many pumping engines were of this type.

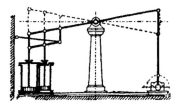

McNaught Compound Beam Engine. This system consisted of a small cylinder (high-pressure cylinder), placed at the opposite end of the beam to the larger cylinder, was introduced by McNaught for increasing the power of existing engines. The high-pressure cylinder was the one added, the original cylinder being the low-pressure cylinder. The power of the engine was thus increased by increase of boiler pressure and the addition of the new small cylinder, to which the boiler was admitted. (See glossary for more details).

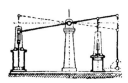

Inclined Frame Engines, used extensively for paddle steamers in several different varieties, usually compound engines.

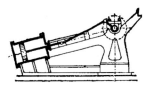

A Double-Cylinder Engine, derived from the above, with the cylinder inclined at an angle of about 45^0, was occasionally used for driving rolling mills in bar iron works.

Radial Engines. (Brotherhood type) A recent type, of which there were many varieties, in both 3 and 4 cylinder configurations. These were used for driving fans, steam launches and other applications requiring speed and compactness.

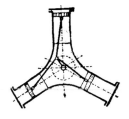

Central Valve Engines (Willans type) A modern design, single acting, compound or triple expansion configuration; a special feature was the hollow piston rod and central valve. Extensively used for driving dynamos coupled direct on to the armature shaft.

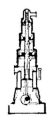

Various ways of arranging cylinders and cranks in double and three-cylinder compound and triple expansion engines

Double cylinder, with cranks at 180^0

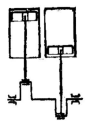

Three-cylinder engine, with cranks at 120^0

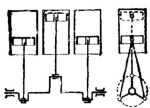

Compound Woolf engine with cranks together

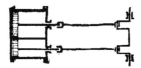

Compound Woolf engine with cranks at 180⁰

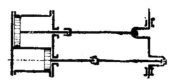

Compound Tandem engine with receiver

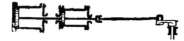

Compound engine with cylinders side by side with receiver cranks at 90⁰

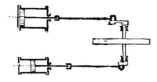

Triple expansion engine with cylinders side by side; cranks at 120⁰

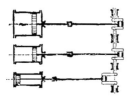

Triple expansion engine, semi-tandem; two cranks at 90⁰

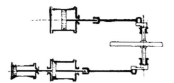

Simple slide valve

This consisted of an inverted metal box sliding on the ported face of the cylinder. It controlled the admission and exhaust of the steam to both ends of the cylinder and exhausted beneath the box valve

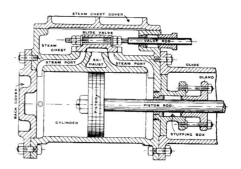

Simple piston valve

This consisted of a turned bobbin, working in a bored liner. It worked on the same principle as the slide valve.

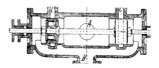

Simple valve gears

These valves were operated by simple eccentric motions of various patterns, and many allowed variable cut-off of the steam as well as reversing.

The Corliss

This was a semi-circular semi-rotating valve working in a bored liner. Separate valves were provided for steam and exhaust at each end of the cylinder, so there were four in number. A trip gear operated the valves.

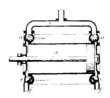

Drop valves

These were circular with taper faces, which fitted upon similar faces fitted to the cylinder. The faces were ground together to make them steam tight. The valves were lifted to admit steam and dropped by the trip gear to cut off the admission. A variety of this pattern was simple bobbins fitted with piston rings.

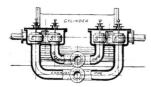

The Uniflow

This had admission valves only since the steam exhausted through a ring of ports in the centre of the cylinder barrel.

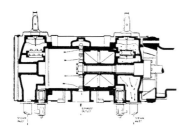

BOILERS

Cornish boilers contained a single flue

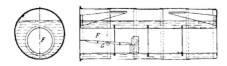

Lancashire boilers contained twin flues

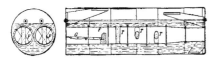

Multitibular boilers were of various types including the locomotive

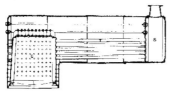

Vertical boilers were of various types. Used in very small plants

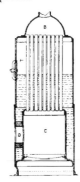

Watertube boilers were of various types.

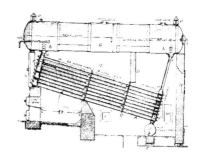

POWER TRANSMISSION

Rope drives, taking power from the engine to the floors of a mill, were usual in textile mills. In older mills power was often transmitted by a vertical shaft.

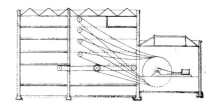

Flat belts of leather or rubberized canvas drove individual machines from a line shaft powered by the rope drive.

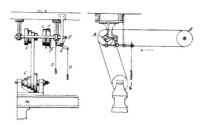

MINING

Winding engines were almost invariably made with two cylinders having cranks at 90^0, allowing good control by the engine driver. A winding engine was required to work intermittently, starting a heavy load from rest, bringing this load up with great velocity, and bringing it to rest again. This had to be done at great speed in a short time, since a great number of winds were needed daily to raise an economic quantity of coal. For this, the engine needed to be powerful and to be under precise control of the engineman at all times.

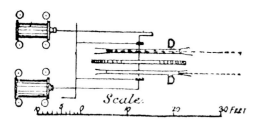

Balancing was done by fixing a rope similar to the winding rope to the bottom of each cage, the rope hanging in a loop down the pit shaft, ensuring a perpetual balance-weight equal to the winding-rope.

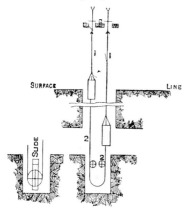

Another method of balancing was by means of the scroll or spiral drum. As the engine proceeded to wind up, the rope was wound in spiral grooves on a continually increasing diameter of drum. The other rope to the descending cage was wound off at an opposing rate so creating a counterbalance. The variation in diameter of the two sides of the drum had the effect of loading the engine proportional to the effort it needed at different stages of the wind.

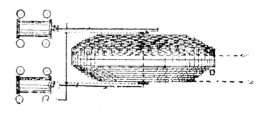

Winding was done by steam, utilising different types of pithead gear.

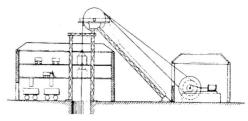

Ventilation was done by various patterns of steam driven rotary fan.

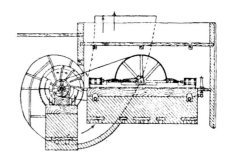

GLOSSARY

Air pump. This removed the condensed water and air contained in the steam. It was normally driven by the engine itself.

Arbor. An axle or spindle.

Barring. This was the action of gently rotating the engine to make possible adjustments during maintenance. It was done by a lever mechanism which engaged in a series of holes cast in the face or side of the flywheel rim. A variation involved a hand or small steam engine-driven gear engaging in gear teeth cast on the inside of the flywheel rim.

Calender. A finishing machine designed to impart lustre and smoothness to woven fabrics. It comprised a series of rolls geared vertically, through which the cloth ran.

Condensers. These were airtight chambers into which the exhaust steam passed for cooling back to warm water. Cooling was by a jet of cold water which mixed with the condensate, or, in the surface type, the cold water passed through a number of small tubes to condense the steam outside them.

Count. The measure of yarns by length and weight stating how many hanks of a given length will weigh a pound: the higher the number, the finer the yarn. There were different units of length for different yarns, e.g. cotton, wool, and jute and, in the wool trade, different locations.

Dram or tram. A wheeled tub for conveying coal at the colliery.

Duff coal. Small coal unsuitable for retail sale. Used for firing boilers at collieries.

Economiser. A system of pre-heating boiler feed-water, using the heat of the waste gases in the boiler flues. First invented in 1843 by Edward Green of Wakefield, Yorks.

Edge tools. These were any kind of hand tool with a sharp cutting edge, such as a spade, hoe, sickle or scythe. A strip of toughened steel was forged as a sandwich between softer metal, and then sharpened. This was an ancient craft, some of the sites utilising water-powered tilt hammers.

Egg-ended boiler. A horizontal cylindrical boiler with hemispherical ends and no flues. At early pattern, superseded by the Cornish and Lancashire types.

Flitches. The two halves of the beam of a beam engine. Originally cast solid, beams were sometimes made in two halves and kept apart by spacers and bolts.

Glands. These were recessed bosses in the cylinder cover or valve chest of a steam engine or pump which were fitted with fibre or metal packing. They allowed the rods to work freely without leaking steam or water.

Governor. This device controlled the speed of the engine, if it was too fast or too slow, by regulating the steam supply. There were many patterns but all depended on rotating weights which adjusted the control mechanism.

Grid. The National Grid, the national electricity supply system, was begun in the 1920s. Before it became very widespread by the 1950s, many small towns and larger businesses generated their own supplies, with varying supply standards.

Hoppit or hoppet. A large basket used in mining.

Lodge. A pond located near a mill's engine-house which held the engine's condensing water. More common where the site was not previously water powered.

Manhattan engine. This was a design which coupled a horizontal and a vertical engine driving to the same crank pin. The idea surfaced around 1870 and reached its zenith in the engines driving the Manhattan (New York) power stations in the early 1900s. A number were made by various makers for use in Britain, driving textile mills, rolling mills and London Tramways power generation.

McNaughting was patented by William McNaught of Glasgow in 1845. Piston loads were thus opposed, so reducing stresses on the beam centre. The fitting of high pressure boilers and compound working gave great economy.

Mule. Cotton spinning machine, invented by Crompton, so named because it incorporated the roller-drawing principle of Arkwright's water frame and the carriage drawing of Hargreave's spinning jenny. The first successful self-acting mule was invented by Richard Roberts 1830.

Non-dead centre engines. These were vertical or horizontal engines in which two parallel cylinders were coupled to a single crank pin by a triangular connecting rod, and had the advantage of starting at almost any crank position. Twin or quadruple cylinder compound engines were common. Their heyday was 1880-1907.

Northrop loom. An automatic loom invented by 1894 by J. H. Northrop in the USA.

Overwinding gear. This was an apparatus to stop a winding engine lifting a cage beyond the pit bank and damaging itself and contents on the pit frame. Various systems were used.

Process steam. This was steam after it had left the engine and before it was condensed. It was used in the plant for other purposes such as central heating, heating dye vats, drying paper.

Rastrick Boiler. A pattern of vertical boiler which utilised the waste heat from wrought iron-making processes.

Ring spinning. A system where the spinning spindle revolves within a ring, with a small steel hoop on the flange of the ring to govern the winding-on of the thread.

Room and Power. The term means that a capitalist established a factory with a power supply (usually steam), and heating, and rented out space to small craftsmen or manufacturers. Each floor had a drive shaft taken from the engine from which individual machines, owned and worked by the tenants, were driven.

Shear. Mechanical scissors used for cropping billets of steel during the rolling process.

Sizing. The stiffening of fabrics with various pastes or starches.

Slow banking. This involved the means of controlling the winding engine carefully to allow precise location of the cage at the finish of the wind.

Tentering or stentering. This was the action of stretching cloth whilst drying to ensure all the threads were in line. Originally done by hand, latterly by machine.

SOURCES

Definitions and illustrations used have been drawn from:

Wilfred Lineham, *A text book of Mechanical Engineering*, 9ed, 1906.

Arnold Lupton, *Mining*, 3ed, 1906.

William S. Murphy, The *Textile Industries*, 8 vol, 1910.

Herman Haeder and H. H. P. Powles, *Handbook on the Steam Engine*, 4ed, 1914.

More detailed technical information about engine design may be found in:

Colin Bowden, 'The stationary steam engine: a critical bibliography', *Industrial Archaeology Review*, XV, (1992-3), pp 177-194.

George Watkins, *The Stationary Steam Engine*, 1968.

George Watkins, *The Textile Mill Engine*, 2 vol, 1970, 1971 (reprinted Landmark Publishing, 1 vol, 1999).

George Watkins, & R. A. Buchanan, *Man and the Steam Engine*, 1975, 2ed 1978.

R. A. Buchanan & George Watkins, *The Industrial Archaeology of the Stationary Steam Engine*, (1976) This is a very authoritative account of the evolution of design and construction.

George Watkins. *The Steam Engine in Industry*, 2 vol, (1978, 1978). The linking passages describing the application of steam to different industries are specially valuable.

Transactions of the Newcomen Society, especially:

Arnold Throp 'Some notes on the history of the Uniflow Steam Engine', vol 43 (1970-71) pp 19-39.

George Watkins, 'The development of the Steam Winding Engine' vol 50, (1978-79), pp 11-24.

James L. Wood, 'The introduction of the Corliss Engine into Britain', vol 52, (1980-81) pp 1-13.

R. L. Hills, 'The Uniflow engine, a re-appraisal' vol 57, (1985-6) , pp 59-77.

R. W. M. Clouston, 'The development of the Babcock Boiler in Britain up to 1939', vol 58, (1986-87), pp 75-87.

James L. Wood. 'The Sulzer steam engine comes to Britain', vol 59, (1987-88), pp 129-152.

Stationary Power (The Journal of the International Steam Engine Society), especially:

William D. Sawyer, Corliss Man and engine, 2 vol, 1994, (JISSES 10), 1997, (JISSES 13).

CORNWALL

1) Pool, South Crofty Tin Mine, Robinson's Engine

SER 814

Type:	Cornish beam pump
Photo taken:	1956
Maker & Date:	Copperhouse Foundry, 1854
Cylinder/dimensions:	80in x 10ft
Hp:?	*Spm:* $11^1/_2$ *Psi:* 40
Service:	Mine pump. Shaft 2,022ft deep

This was one of the best engines in Cornwall, now preserved on site by the National Trust. Designed by Grose, it has his feature of the steam and equilibrium valves opposite to each other on the cylinder. Built for £2,700 it was hard worked until replaced by electric pumps in 1955. It worked also at Crenver and Owen Vean, and finally went to South Crofty in 1903, working there continuously until replaced by the electric pumps. It was the last Cornish engine to work at a Cornish metal mine.

DEVON

2) Bovey Tracey, Kelly Mine

SER 1463

Type:	California stamps etc
Photo taken:	1974
Maker & Date:	No other data
Cylinder/dimensions:	No other data
Service:	Processed minerals from mine

Kelly was a small unit working diatomaceous earth from the shafts and galleries of the mine. The machinery included a haulage winch, air compressor and 4 head of stamps, almost certainly the last examples of that type, with cams at the side of the lifters that turn the stamp heads as they lift them. The framing, indeed the whole construction, was of timber, and everything belt driven from a Blackstone oil engine of the 1920s, and a water turbine, possibly a Turgoside jet–type, seen beside the rough steps on the right; the oil engine is behind the stamps. Worked over many years, the product was valuable for camouflage colour–wash during the War. Production probably ceased in the 1960s since when the plant has been vandalised of almost every piece of brass. The stamps justify preservation in view of their rarity.

3) Uffculme, Fox Bros, Coldharbour Mill

SER 1114

Type:	Horizontal cross compound
Photo taken:	1962
Maker & Date:	Pollit and Wigzell, Sowerby Bridge, 1910
Cylinder/dimensions:	13in and 26in x 3ft 0in – Drop and Corliss valves
Hp: 320	*Rpm:* 90 *Psi:* 135
Service:	Woollen preparation. 13 rope driven to mill shafts driven by water wheel

The mill appears to have been entirely water driven until 1910, when the Pollit engine was installed. The water power system had been greatly modified before by taking the tail race of the water wheel over 300 yards downstream to increase the available fall at the water-wheel from 9ft 6in to 14ft 6in. The water wheel and the engine were in regular use in 1973, with rope drives to couple the two power sources to drive the whole mill. The vertical shaft of the original water power drive was changed to drive the lower floors and a new wool combing shed at the rear by belts later on. A water turbine was installed but was soon replaced in the 1880s, possibly when the water power system was altered.

3

DORSET

4) *Blandford Forum, J. L. Marsh, Brewery*   SER 234a

Type:	Table engine non–condensing
Photo taken:	1938
Maker & Date:	Unknown, c.1850?
Cylinder/dimensions:	6in x 1ft 0in – Slide valve
	5ft 6in to engine top. Flywheel 4ft 6in diameter
Hp:	*Rpm:* *Psi:*
Service:	Pump drives by belt to countershaft

Unaltered in over 80 years of work, nothing was known of this, but it was believed to have been supplied new to the brewery. The four fluted columns to support the table were an unusual feature, as, too, was the use of adjustable slide blocks for the cross-head guides, and the circular shape of the crosshead guide frames. The circular section flywheel rim with spokes cast in and the external steam ports were features that were largely disused by 1850.

5) *Blandford Forum, J. L. Marsh Brewery*   SER 234b

Type:	Table engine
Photo taken:	1938
Maker & Date:	Unknown, c.1875?
Cylinder/dimensions:	6in x 1ft 3in – Slide valve
	6ft 3in high. Flywheel 4ft 6in diameter
Hp:	*Rpm:* *Psi:*
Service:	Chaff cutter drive in stables

Much more modern than SER 234a, this was completely different in design. The crank shaft was at the mid level of the table supports, with twin crank pin bearings, whilst the fitting of two crankshaft bearings made it independent, whereas SER 234a with a single bearing in the bed required an outer bearing placed in the engine room wall.

6) *Blandford St Mary, Hall & Woodhouse, Brewery*   SER 1425

Type:	Horizontal single cylinder
Photo taken:	1971
Maker & Date:	Gimson & Co., Leicester. Date possibly 1899
Cylinder/dimensions:	12in x 2ft 0in – Slide valve
Hp: About 25	*Rpm:* 100 *Psi:* 75
Service:	Plant drive by 11in belt off 24in pulley

This was probably supplied by Gimsons when, in a reorganization, they supplied a mashing tun and rousers and probably other brewing plant. At one time it was heavily loaded, but now mainly drives the rousers and malt and grain elevators. There had also been another engine for grinding the malt and hoists etc., but only the Gimson remained in 1971, and it was in daily use. A Rider–type semi–rotating cutoff valve was fitted on the main slide valve back, which was at one time under the control of the governor, but latterly a Pickering throttling governor was fitted, with the Rider valve in the main chest on fixed cutoff. As the photograph shows it is well kept as indeed is all of the plant in the breweries everywhere.

7) Bournemouth, G. Jennings & Co., The Potteries, Parkstone SER 956

Type:	Horizontal single cylinder condensing
Photo taken:	1958
Maker & Date:	Thornewill & Warham, Burton on Trent, 1919
Cylinder/dimensions:	About 27in x 3ft 6in – Corliss valves
Hp: About 180	*Rpm:* 80 *Psi:* 120
Service:	Works drive by ropes and alternators

This was supplied new in 1919, and drove the clay preparation and works plant by ropes, to two shafts, as well as two alternators also by ropes. The exhaust steam was used for the preliminary drying of the prepared pottery work before firing in the kilns. A great range of chimney and other pots was made and tiles. The steam plant continued to run until it was closed about 1964. The engine had needed very little attention in some 40 years of hard work and the design was typical of the extensive machine finish which was usual in later years. There was also a Belliss & Morcom twin cylinder engine as a standby, but it was not greatly used.

8) Bridport, J. C. & R. H. Palmer, The Old Brewery   SER 1459a

Type:	Inverted vertical single cylinder non–condensing
Photo taken:	1973
Maker & Date:	Brown & May, Devizes, c.1900s
Cylinder/dimensions:	About 9in x 1ft 0in – Slide valve
Hp: About 10	*Rpm:* 100 *Psi:* 60
Service:	Plant drive by belt

Replacing an earlier engine, this was on the first floor of the buildings, and was certainly there before 1945, and probably secondhand when installed. The early engine type is unknown. This is a fairly late example of Brown & May's work, and the design is interesting in that the main frame is a fine casting, comprising the engine frame with the trunk guides and crankshaft bearings in a single casting, so requiring good machining facility to complete it. The bent crankshaft is a fine forging, and throughout, the engine, which appears to be unaltered, is a good country workshop product, which having given many years of service, should continue thus. It drives into the general shafting from which the brewery pumps, malt crusher, conveyors, etc. are driven, although the mashing rousers are electrically driven now. The undershot water wheel also drives into the same shafting and this is largely used for filling the brewery water supply tanks. Mineral waters were also made at one time, but not recently; there are numerous motor drives in the brewery. The boiler, a Cochran vertical, is stoker fired.

9) Bridport, J. C. & R.H. Palmer, The Old Brewery   SER 1459b

Type:	Beer fermenting vats
Photo taken:	1973
Maker & Date:	Wilson and Co., Wilson & Scotchman, Frome
Cylinder/dimensions:	No applicable data
Service:	Beer processing

Breweries are extremely well kept and clean, using far more water for this than for beer production, and this is typical of all. The fermenting stage is very important, needing close watching and temperature control for the correct final gravity and flavour. It is at this stage that yeast is produced, and is skimmed off, and the seven vats were fitted with patent skimmers made by Griffin & Co., Kingston Ironworks, Bath. No dates were known and in any case frequent changes of plant made precise dating difficult, unless noted on the item. It is probable that Wilsons regularly fitted the Griffin skimmers as long as they were made. Throughout, the Frome craftsmanship was of the highest standards.

10) Charminster, Herrison Mental Hospital   SER 488a

Type:	4 Willans simple expansion engines
Photo taken:	1952
Maker & Date:	3 = Willans & Robinson, Thames Ditton, 1895
	1 = Willans & Robinson, Rugby, 1904
Cylinder/dimension:	3 = 10in x 5in; later = 12in x 6in – Central piston valve
*Hp:*No data	*Rpm:* *Psi:*
Service:	Electricity and heat supply

The hospital was lighted by electricity in 1895, and heated by the exhaust steam from the earlier three engines. The use of simple expansion Willans engines was unusual but with the demand for low pressure steam for heating the economy was not a serious matter. Carbon arc lamps were used for the lighting until 1926, and copper gauze brushes, but this was then changed to carbon brushes and filament lamps. The dynamos were by Newtons of Taunton, and were carrying 25% overload when 60 years old. A diesel engine was added later, but the whole of the private plant was scrapped in the 1950s when the entire system was replaced by alternating current taken from the Grid system.

11) Charminster, Herrison Mental Hospital   SER 488b

Type:	Willans engine dismantled
Photo taken:	1952
Maker & Date:	Willans & Robinson No. 1832, 1895
Cylinder/dimensions:	No data available
Hp:	*Rpm:* *Psi:*
Service:	

This shows several of the unusual features of the design. Note that the eccentric for the piston valve drive is on the crank pin with the connecting rod bearing on either side as seen in the right hand crank. At the left can be seen one of the piston valve lines, with the lower guide and above it the base for the piston valve which operated within the trunk seen attached to the large buffer piston beyond it. The two piston valves can be seen near to the flywheel, and the valve line for the right hand engine is at the front of the bed, the piston valve fitting upon the slender rod at the top of it. Near it on the bed are the two bottom connecting rod end bearings for the left hand engine.

12) Dorchester, Dorchester Water Works   SER 4b

Type:	Woolf compound house–built beam
Photo taken:	1932
Maker & Date:	The Coalbrookdale Co., 1880?
Cylinder/dimensions:	16in x 4ft 0in and 24in x 5ft 6in – Slide valves
Hp:	*Rpm:* *Psi:*
Service:	Beside the above separate well and pumping 450,000 gallons per day. 1 Cornish boiler 21ft 0in x 6ft 0in

This performed a similar service to SER 4a, but was in complete contrast. House–built, it was very plain, with a single web cast iron beam, forged steel connecting rod, and with the entablature built into the walls. This meant that it was carried across, and under the upper framing of SER 4a. The circular supporting columns were quite plain.

13) Poole, J.T. Sydenham & Co., Sawmills   SER 1374

Type:	Horizontal cross compound condensing
Photo taken:	1969
Maker & Date:	Wren & Hopkinson, Manchester, 1880s
Cylinder/dimensions:	10in and 18in x 2ft 0in – Slide valves
Hp: 60–70	*Rpm:* 90 *Psi:* 80
Service:	Machinery drive by 10in belt from 6ft pulley

The engine was probably made about 1880, possibly came to Poole then, and was bought by Sydenhams around 1888. The Galloway boiler was also secondhand, made in 1888, and previously worked at a margarine factory. The condenser was below the crosshead guides originally, and was altered to the later tandem system by the Dorset Foundry Co., Poole, when moved to Sydenhams. It continued to run part of the works later, even when much machinery was motor driven. The final changeover to all electrical drives came in 1969, when the engine was secured by the Poole Technical College for preservation. It is one of the very few small Lancashire engines to survive.

14) Poole, Sewage Pumping Station   SER 957

Type:	Two horizontal three cylinder compound. Non–condensing
Photo taken:	1958
Maker & Date:	Goddard, Massey & Warner, Nottingham, 1902
Cylinder/dimensions:	15in, 16in and 16in x 2ft 0in – Slide valves
Hp: 60-70?	*Rpm:* 24 max *Psi:* 100
Service:	Sewage lift by ram pumps

These were very unusual with three cranks and compound working, yet the simplest that could be designed for reasonable economy at the time. The photograph shows the disc cranks on the outer cylinder with a slotted double webbed one for the middle cylinder, with only three bearings for the crankshaft. One engine was always at work, as clearing depended on them, but at times they had to run as low as 5 rpm, and three cranks allowed this without stopping. The pumps, as the engines, were very simple, and little ever seemed to have been needed to keep them running until they, with the similar air compressors and Cornish boilers, were scrapped when electrically driven plant was installed in the early 1960s.

15) Tarrant Gunville, Mr J. Dyer (Farmer)   SER 536

Type:	Compound traction
Photo taken:	1953
Maker & Date:	Fodens Ltd., Sandbach. No. 9052, 1914
Cylinder/dimensions:	Sizes unknown
Hp: No data	*Rpm:* *Psi:*
Service:	Farm hire

This was believed to be the last traction engine made by Fodens, and was to be pre-served in the 1950s, in fact still used as needed then, although custom threshing was reduced. It was a typical Foden's design with the multiple spokes in the rear wheels, and the small belly tank appeared to be original. An interesting feature was a separate exhaust pipe for the high pressure cylinder when running double high pressure. Late in date this had not been as heavily used as many of the threshing traction engines.

16) *Weymouth, Devenish Weymouth Brewery*   SER 1457

Type:	Horizontal single cylinder non–condensing
Photo taken:	1973
Maker & Date:	Barrett, Exall, and Andrewes, Reading Ironworks, 1860s?
Cylinder/dimensions:	11in x 1ft 3in – Slide valve
Hp: About 10	*Rpm:* 100 *Psi:* 60
Service:	Drove brewery plant by 6in belt

Although early, this was probably not the first engine in the plant, since a vertical engine said to have been purchased from the 1851 Exhibition was preserved in the brewery until that part was destroyed by enemy action in World War II. The horizontal engine is now preserved where it worked, and may well be the last made by this concern in existence. It is quite complete with all of the features noted in Bourne's *Catechism on the Steam Engine,* such as the circular section crosshead guide bars, set screw adjusted main–bearings, open type eccentric sheaves, bent forged crankshaft, and slow speed governor. It had driven various units, ie. the malt crusher, conveyors, pumps, and possibly the brewing rousers originally, duties which were taken by the later horizontal engine, (possibly early 1900s) which is to be preserved beside this one, in the old engine room.

HAMPSHIRE

17) *Aldershot, Symonds Flour Mill*   SER 672

Type:	Horizontal cross compound condensing
Photo taken:	1954
Maker & Date:	Scott & Hodgson, Guide Bridge, nr Manchester No 218, 1923
Cylinder/dimensions:	14in and 28in x 3ft – Drop valves
Hp: 300	*Rpm:* 90 *Psi:* 160
Service:	Drove flour mill

The illustration copied from the makers' catalogue is identical to Symonds engine, and shows Scott's latest engine design. The mill was closed and all plant scrapped about 1954, and only the nameplate is preserved. Plain and simple, it was highly efficient and gave little trouble in 40 years of running night and day – 120 hours per week. The bored trunk guides and main bearings were a single casting on each side, and the cylinders were bolted to a faced end at the back of the guides. It was all fitted to a single bed casting on each side, with the circular condenser on an extension on the left hand side. The steam was superheated to 550°F.

18) *Andover, Watson & Haig, Engineer & Contractor*   SER 535

Type:	Single cylinder traction
Photo taken:	1953
Maker & Date:	Wallis & Steevens, Andover. Date unknown
Cylinder/dimensions:	No data
Hp:	*Rpm:* *Psi:*
Service:	Hire and haulage

This was the standard Wallis expansion engine, with a governor controlled cut–off slide valve. These were widely used for threshing, and were economical and ran steadily. Although heavily used, little but tube replacements had been required. This type was much used for threshing corn, as well as hauling, but it was probably scrapped with the trend toward combine harvesting developing in the 1950s.

19) Basingstoke, Sewage Pumping Station   SER 1207

Type:	Two horizontal single cylinder condensing
Photo taken:	1965
Maker & Date:	Tanges Ltd, Birmingham, 1911
Cylinder/dimensions:	18in x 2ft 0in – Slide valves
Hp: 100	*Rpm:* 20 *Psi:* 75
Service:	Pumped sewage to treatment station

As at Eastbourne, the power to pump the sewage was provided by burning the town refuse in incinerators, with Babcock & Wilcox water tube boilers. Each engine was run for 19–20 hours per day, for a week at a time. The units were in tandem, with the condenser following the steam cylinder and the ram sewage lifting pumps behind this. The refuse incinerators were built by Manlove, Alliotts of Nottingham and were very effective until the heating value of the refuse decreased as house coal fires were abandoned. The load had also grown greatly, and it was necessary to install electrically driven pumps in the 1960s, and dump the rubbish on tips. The engines would have been preserved, but a home could not be found in time and they were scrapped. The plant was very well kept.

20) Havant, Portsmouth Waterworks, Havant Pumping Station
SER 10b

Type:	Three triple expansion drop valve engines
Photo taken:	1934
Maker & Date:	Worthington Simpson, Newark, 1926
Cylinder/dimensions:	Sizes unknown
Hp:	*Rpm:* *Psi:*
Service:	Town supply, surface to reservoirs, 5 million gallons per day each?

The early Farlington supply was shut down in the 1920s, when the supply from Havant, until then provided by Worthington horizontal pumps, was greatly increased by the triples. These in turn were superseded by electric units about 1960.

21) Horndean, George Gale & Co., Brewery   SER 1451

Type:	Inverted vertical double cylinder simple
Photo taken:	1972
Maker & Date:	Unknown, c.1900?
Cylinder/dimensions:	7$\frac{1}{2}$in x 9in – Slide valves
Hp: About 20	*Rpm:* 90 *Psi:* 100
Service:	Brewery plant drive by belts

This was believed to be an old ferry–boat engine, made about 1900 and installed by Gales in 1949. There appears to have been a similar engine, or an older type there before, as this engine was coupled to the old flywheel shaft, and the older engine almost certainly had a low level crankshaft. It appeared to be a marine engine, having brackets cast on the columns for a reversing weigh shaft for the link motion, but although there was only one eccentric for each cylinder, there was no keyway in the shaft for the other eccentric necessary for Stephenson's link motion. Certainly there had long been mechanical drives for the pumps, rousers, malt crushing and elevating within the plant. It was a very old brewery site in use some two centuries or more.

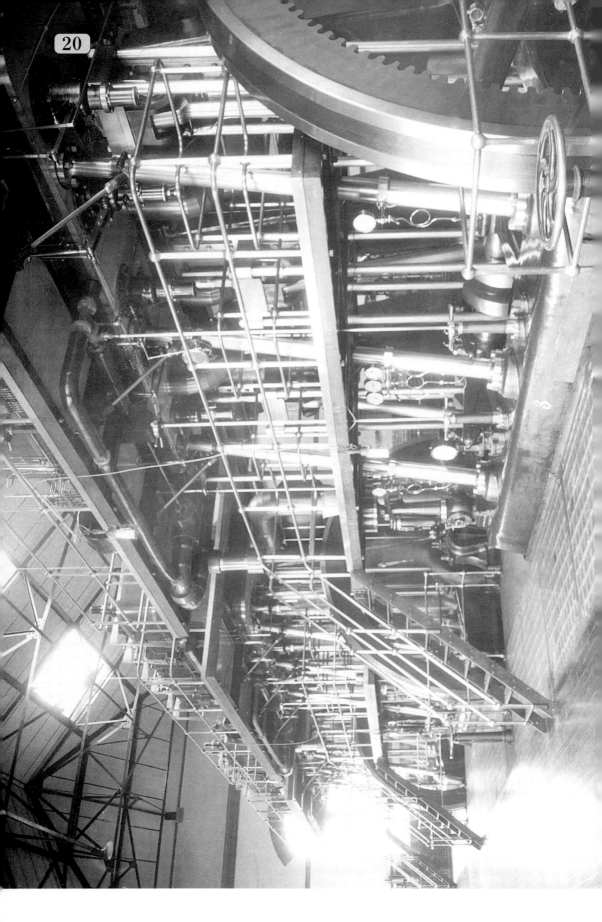

22) Horndean, George Gale & Co., Brewery — SER 1451a

Type:	Inverted vertical single cylinder, forced lubrication
Photo taken:	1972
Maker & Date:	Belliss and Morcom, Birmingham, 1950s?
Cylinder/dimensions:	7in x 5in – Piston valve
Hp: 18	*Rpm:* 470 *Psi:* 120
Service:	Plant drive

This was added in the early 1950's, purchased new, and was connected to the original line shafts by a 6in belt. Latterly, the engines had mainly driven the well pump for the water supply, the well being near to the engine room. With much new plant, the drive pattern was changed to electric motors, so that the Belliss also was standby by 1972.

23) Otterbourne, Southampton Waterworks, Otterbourne Pumping Station — SER 1376a

Type:	Two inverted vertical triple expansion condensing
Photo taken:	1969
Maker & Date:	Worthington Simpson, Newark 1926, No 5039–40
Cylinder/dimensions:	18in, 24in & 56in x 4ft 0in – Drop valves
Hp:	*Rpm:* *Psi:*
Service:	Water supply from wells to reservoir

The two engines drew the water from a single well, each engine driving the two sets of pump rods from wooden spear rods and bell cranks from a single crank on the end of the crankshaft of the engine. This can be seen in the photograph, with the single crank outside of the engine flywheel of the engine which is standing. They were Worthington–Simpson's latest design, highly economical when using superheated steam, and regularly run for many months on end. In later years, increasing demands often led to the two engines being run at the same time in some areas, but this did not occur here. The main water load had been taken by other pumping stations, and by electrically driven or diesel driven plant, and the several steam stations were thus scrapped. Otterbourne finally stopped the steam sets about 1971, and they will be scrapped. There is one by Hathorn, Davey at Twyford station, which though superseded may be saved. The pump layout is similar to Otterbourne.

24) Otterbourne, Southampton Waterworks, Otterbourne Pumping Station — SER 1376b

Type:	Vertical & horizontal shaft steam turbines
Photo taken:	1969
Maker & Date:	W.H. Allen & Co., Bedford, 1936
Cylinder/dimensions:	No relevant sizes
Hp: See below	*Rpm:* 6–8500 *Psi:* 200
Service:	As SER1376a

These were the last steam sets to be installed by the Southampton Water Authority, and although using more steam were cheaper to purchase and install and required minimum space and housing cost. The vertical spindle set at the left drove the submerged pump in the well, and was about 150 hp, running at about 6,500 rpm. The surface lift pumps at the right required twice the power, i.e. 297 hp, and ran at 6,000 to 8,500 rpm driving the two pumps in series. Both of the turbines were served from a single surface condenser behind, placed in the water circuit of the two surface lift pumps. Otterbourne illustrated by examples, three stages of steam pumping, as there were also in the 1960s two of the four original Simpson compound beam engines (see SER 230 and SER 1376c) The whole of the steam plant will however be scrapped in the early 1970s when the load will be taken electrically.

25) Otterbourne, Southampton Waterworks, Otterbourne Pumping Station   SER 1376c

Type:	Two Woolf compound rotative beam
Photo taken:	1969
Maker & Date:	James Simpson & Co., Pimlico, London, 1886
Cylinder/dimensions:	Data see SER230
Hp:	*Rpm:* *Psi:*
Service:	As 1376a

These are included here to illustrate the difference between the earlier classic beam pumping engine, and the later triple expansion turbine . The relative capacities were beam, $1^1/_4$ gallons per day, the triple expansions $5^1/_2$ million gallons per day each, and the steam turbine $3^1/_2$ million gallons daily. The turbines were in the space on the other side of the beam engine house wall and one of the valve positions can be seen through the window aperture. The very fine condition of all of the plant is the usual condition, as my visit was not expected. Then pumps were driven by the rods projecting downwards from the beam.

26) Otterbourne, Southampton Waterworks, Otterbourne Pumping Station   SER 230

Type:	Two Woolf compound beam
Photo taken:	1938
Maker & Date:	James Simpson & Co., 1895
Cylinder/dimensions:	$28^1/_2$in x 4ft 9in – Slide valves
	$38^1/_2$in x 7ft 0in – Drop valves
	Beam 23ft 0in long. Flywheel 18ft 0in diameter
Service:	Town supply from wells. Pumps driven off beam near crank

There were four of these engines, A, B, C, and D, two of which were removed in the 1930s to make room for the Allen turbine units. The beam engines were plain substantial sets which gave little trouble but were superseded, owing to the demand for more water. The beams were of cast iron, but the pump and connecting rods were of steel. The use of slide valves on the high pressure, and drop valves on the low pressure cylinders was unusual. The beams were followed by the triples of 1925, and the Allen turbine sets of 1936, after which all was diesel electric, largely in the new station.

27) Portsmouth, Eastney Sewage Pumping Station   SER 486

Type:	Two Woolf compound beam
Photo taken:	1952
Maker & Date:	James. Watt & Co., Birmingham, 1887
Cylinder/dimensions:	20in x 4ft 6in and 30in x 6ft 0in – Piston valves
Hp: 150 each	*Rpm:* 18–24 *Psi:* 60
Service:	Low level sewage lift to sea

The sewers entered the station at low level and one engine had to operate continuously to avoid flooding. There were two plunger pumps driven off the engine beams, discharging about 250,000 gallons per hour to 10–15ft. head originally. The engines were overhauled by Hathorn, Davey in 1926, which raised the capacity to 325,000 gallons per hour per engine. They were superseded in 1954 by electrically driven pumps as the load had grown greatly. They are to be preserved on site if possible, but the sea air is a difficulty, causing rusting.

28) *Southwick, Golden Lion Hotel, Home Brewery*   SER 1378

Type:	Horizontal single cylinder
Photo taken:	1969
Maker & Date:	Unknown
Cylinder/dimensions:	6in x 10in – Slide valve
Hp: 10	*Rpm:* 120 *Psi:* 80
Service:	Plant drive by 5in belt

The Home Brewery was a complete plant said to have evolved from brewing in a nearby cellar. It was developed by one man who, with a special brew formula (which incidentally he would not pass on at his decease) secured a trade with public houses that employed two horses and drays on delivery locally. No positive dates are known but the boiler was a Lumby centre flue of 1947, and probably not the original one. The little plant was very compact, with the direct fired brewing copper on the upper floor, and the engine drove the malt crusher, rousers, elevators etc. All was of the simplest design, and had served well, employing half a dozen men in an area where there was little but farming. It is hoped that the whole will be preserved intact as almost the only surviving example of a home brewery.

29) *Timsbury, Southampton Waterworks, Timsbury Pumping Station* SER 8a

Type:	Woolf compound house built beam
Photo taken:	1934
Maker & Date:	Bryan Donkin, London, 1897
Cylinder/dimensions:	Sizes unknown – Slide valves?
Hp:	*Rpm:* *Psi:*
Service:	Town supply to a reservoir 12 miles away. Two plunger pumps driven off the beam. No well?

This was a very unusual design since the twin supporting columns for the beam centre bearings were inclined inward toward the top; they were vertical as a rule. There were two of these engines, one replaced by a diesel engine about 1935. The neat fluted columns and parallel motion were a good example of the late period of beam engine construction.

30) *Timsbury, Southampton Waterworks, Timsbury Pumping Station* SER 8b

Type:	A-frame Woolf compound beam
Photo taken:	1934
Maker & Date:	Easton & Anderson, 1876
Cylinder/dimensions:	18in x 2ft 3in and 24in x 3ft 0in – Slide valves. Beams 9ft 6in long. Flywheel 14ft 0in diameter
Hp:?	*Rpm:* up to 45 *Psi:* 80
Service:	Town supply from wells to reservoirs. Each engine drove a set of three throw well, and a similar set of surface force pumps, $8^1/_2$in x 2ft 0in

Each engine drove its own well and force pumps by a cast iron pinion on the crankshaft 3ft 0in diameter, and a 6ft 0in mortise toothed gear wheel on each of the two pump shafts. The water was hard, and was softened between the two sets of pumps, and each engine was a completely independent unit.

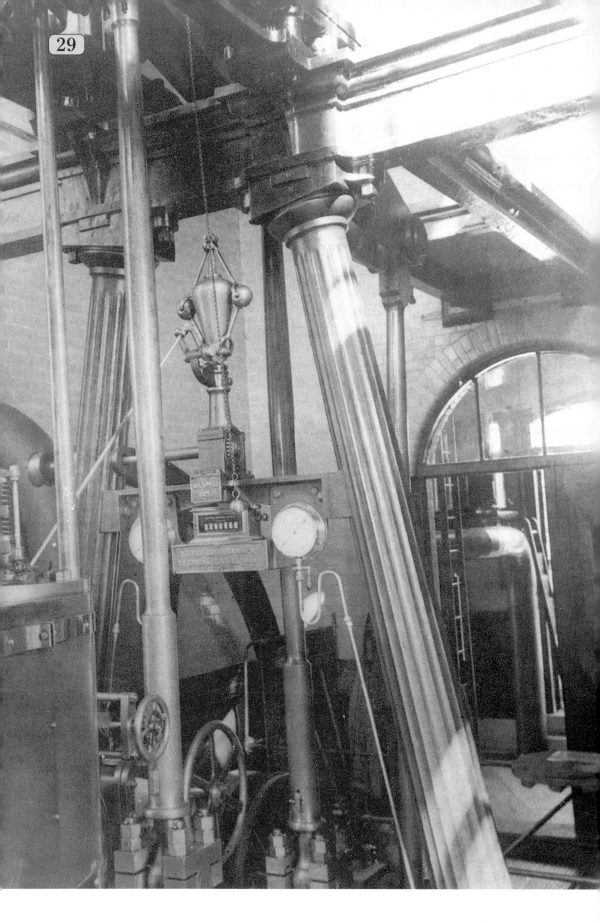

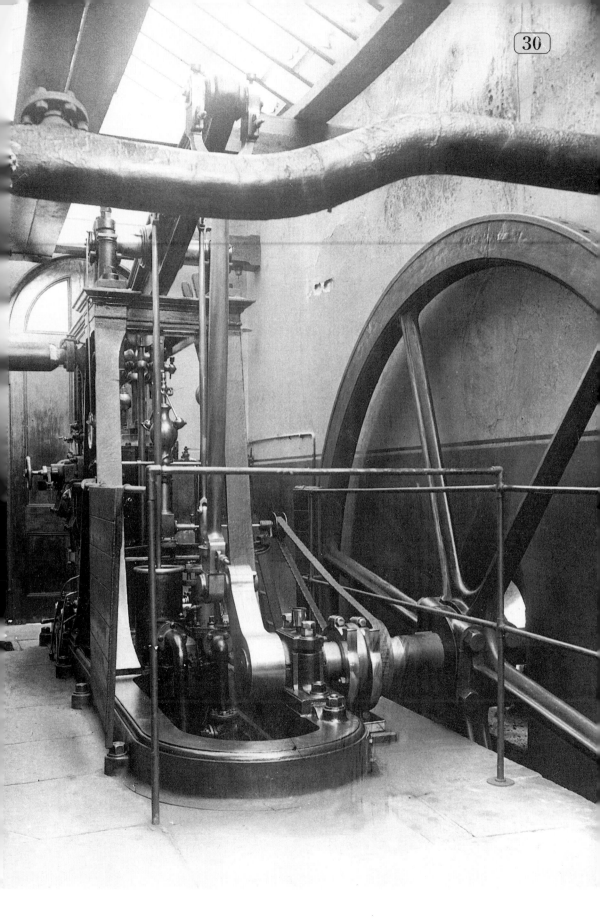

31) Timsbury, Southampton Waterworks, Timsbury Pumping Station
SER 8c

Type:	Two sets of three pumps
Photo taken:	1934
Maker & Date:	
Cylinder/dimensions:	
Hp:	*Rpm:* 24 *Psi:*
Service:	One pumped from wells, other to reservoirs

The water was from wells in the chalk, and each of the two engines was fitted with two sets of pumps, which were driven by a cast iron pinion, driving a mortise toothed gear wheel on each pump crankshaft. The pumps were 8¹/₂ inches diameter, by 2ft. stroke, and ran at 24 rpm. One three throw set on each engine pumped from the well to the Clark's water softening plant, and the other set on each engine pumped the softened water to the town service reservoirs 12 miles away. It was a fine example of a small municipal plant of the type developed for the early town water supply services to meet Health Act provisions. The wooden teeth in the large wheels were held by metal pins in the rim of the wheels, and the crankshafts, bent from a single iron bar, were superb smith's craft. All was scrapped when the power plant was reorganized.

32) Twyford, Southampton Waterworks, Twyford Pumping Station
SER 1377

Type:	Inverted vertical triple expansion
Photo taken:	1969
Maker & Date:	Hathorn, Davey & Co, Leeds, No 6579, 1916?
Cylinder/dimensions:	Corliss valves
Hp:	*Rpm:* *Psi:*
Service:	Town supply from well

The immaculate condition is again apparent. There was another engine of another make and about 1905 date, beside this to the right, and this was removed to make space for the electrically driven pumps which now carry the load. There are many similarities between the Davey and the Worthington–Simpson units, but the Davey has the Corliss valves driven from a camshaft at high level through the delightful Craig trip gear. There were three Babcock & Wilcox water tube boilers for the two engines, but these were to be removed in 1972. It is hoped that the Davey may remain but this is not certain.

33) Winchester, Winchester Sewage Works, Garnier Road Pumping Station
SER 233a

Type:	Two single cylinder beam
Photo taken:	1938
Maker & Date:	Gimson & Co., Leicester, 1878
Cylinder/dimensions:	24in x 5ft 0in – Meyer valves
	Beams 20ft 0in long. Flywheel 20ft 0in diameter
Service:	Refuse destructor steam drove the sewage pumps off the beam engines

These were the main pumps in the 1930s, with the Worthingtons as standby. The beam flitches were moulded inside and out, which was unusual, and the parallel motion was notable for the very long radius rods, working backwards from the pump crossheads. The pumps were driven directly off the beams.

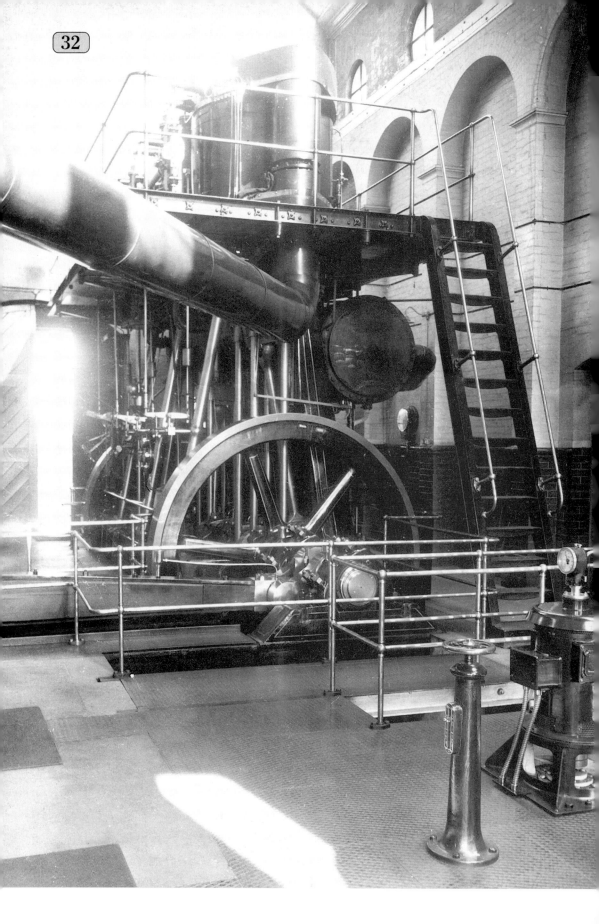

34) Winchester, Winchester Sewage Works, Garnier Road Pumping Station   SER 233b

Type:	Vertical triple expansion non–rotative
Photo taken:	1938
Maker & Date:	Worthington Simpson & Co., Newark & London, 1905
Cylinder/dimensions:	Sizes unknown – Semi–rotative valves
	20ft 0in high to the top – about 2ft 6in stroke
Service:	Standby sets to SER 233a. Plunger pumps. 2 million
	gallons per day – 200ft head

The steam for the station was supplied by Babcock & Wilcox water tube boilers fired by the refuse destructors, and these supplied steam to the beam and the Worthington sets. In the 1930s the beam engines were usually in use, but the horizontal, and vertical Worthingtons were available. The station was reorganized about 1956, when new destructors, with a Babcock boiler supplying steam to Sisson engines were fitted, which run in conjunction with the oil engine driven ram pumps.

35) Winchester, Winchester Waterworks, Romsey Road Pumping Station   SER 232

Type:	Woolf compound A-frame beam	
Photo taken:	1938	
Maker & Date:	Lilleshall Co., Oakengates, 1885	
Cylinder/dimensions:	Sizes unknown. LP stroke 5ft 6in	
	Beam 18ft 0in long. Flywheel 15ft 0in diameter	
Hp:	*Rpm:*	*Psi:*
Service:	Town supply from well 175ft deep. Pump 145ft below floor	

Ornate and well finished, this was mounted on a bed plate above the floor. There were three eccentrics, one for each main and the expansion valve; this was unusual, as was the massive forged bridle to drive the valves from the upper end of the valve chest. The other engine was an Easton & Anderson of 1877, pumping from the well with two lift pumps $16^{1}/_{2}$in x 2ft 0in pumping 900 gallons per minute.

36) Winchester, Winchester Gasworks   SER 231

Type:	Single grasshopper beam	
Photo taken:	1938	
Maker & Date:	Easton & Anderson, 1892	
Cylinder/dimensions:	About 19in x 1ft 6in – Meyer slide valve	
	Beam 5ft 0in long. Flywheel 5ft 0in diameter	
Hp: 25	*Rpm:* 50	*Psi:* 60
Service:	Exhauster drive. Belt to countershaft	

Typical of Eastons later design, very plain and largely of cast iron, this had the marine type motion ends which they later adopted. It was interesting as it was small for a condensing unit, also in that small condensing engines were uncommon in gas works. The main valve eccentric was keyed to the crankshaft, with the expansion valve eccentric bolted to it.

ISLE OF WIGHT

37) *Cowes, E. Cole & Sons, Shambler's Yard, Ship Repairers* SER 1375

Type:	Grasshopper non–condensing
Photo taken:	1969
Maker & Date:	J.P. Almond, North Shields, 1870s (?)
Cylinder/dimensions:	12in x 2ft 3in stroke – Slide valve
Hp: About 8–10	*Rpm:* 50 *Psi:* 60
Service:	Slipway haulage for repairing vessels

The engine was probably made by a shipyard for general driving, or possibly for a slipway haulage in the North. Steam was supplied by a small Lancashire boiler for many years, but this was condemned in the 1950s, after which it was driven by an air compressor used for portable tool drives, on the slipway. Seen at the extreme left, the engine is very simple, but had the characteristics of the North Country sweep for the lever for hand operation of the slide valve. The flywheel is the early type with wrought iron arms cast into the rim and boss, and generally it is mid 19th century in design but with a more modern slide valve and valve chest. It is very little used and may survive for many years, as it would not pay to replace it. The speed reduction to the slipway hauling cable is about 288 to 1. The cable pulls the carriage with the vessel upon it, out of the water upon rails.

38) *Newport, Ernest Taylor, Albany Steam Museum*   SER 1473

Type:	Horizontal single cylinder non–condensing
Photo taken:	1974
Maker & Date:	Pollit & Wigzell, 1890
Cylinder/dimensions:	13in x 2ft 6in – Rider slide valve
Hp: 50	*Rpm:* 120 *Psi:* 80
Service:	Private museum with many exhibits, but all sold about 1975

Pollits made a number of small single cylinder engines, usually with Rider semi circular cut–off valves under governor control. The general design followed Pollits with the circular upswept bed, rounded crank webs, and governor with the globular counterweight. The single slipper guide was unusual for Pollits ,as most had twin slippers on each side of the bed. The engine was supplied new to Moreys timber yard through a Gloucester contractor, and worked regularly for 70 years until electrically driven machines were installed. It was sold to the local authority for preservation in 1975.

SOMERSET

39) *Bath, Bath Gas Works, North Engine House*   SER 1322

Type:	Various horizontal and high speed inverted vertical steam sets
Photo taken:	1967
Maker & Date:	Waller, Donkin, Belliss etc.
Service:	Exhausters and boosters for gas supply

The station was unusual in that the engines were condensing, whereas most gas works had non–condensing sets. The plant was mixed, containing three of the old horizontal open type single cylinder sets, together with one Belliss high speed enclosed engine with a Roots type booster, and four Belliss engines driving Belliss piston type gas compressors. On the right can be seen one of the older horizontal sets with two Beale type boosters followed by the Belliss with the Roots blower type booster, with other horizontals farther away. The four later Belliss sets are arranged three on the left side, and one at the opposite end. It was very compact yet accessible, as the house was quite large. It was superseded as coal gas

production was run down, and the later engines were diesel with semi–radial piston type compressors all arranged in a separate house. The North house was to be scrapped with the nearly new vertical retorts, as the works were phased out to become a gas holding station, possibly with butane enrichment.

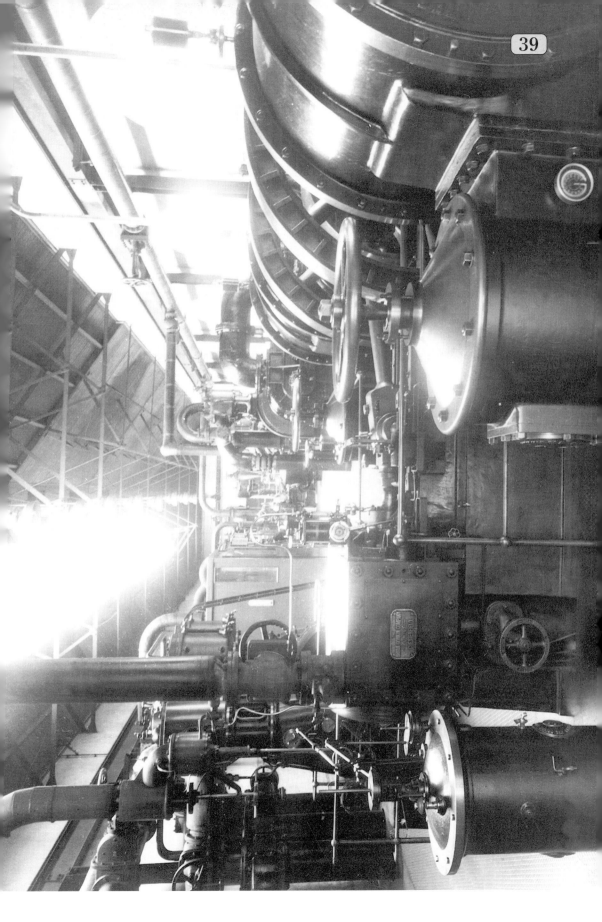

39

40) Bath, Bath Gas Works, North Engine House — SER 1322b

Type:	Belliss C type compound
Photo taken:	1967
Maker & Date:	Belliss & Morcom, Birmingham, No 8282, 1929
Cylinder/dimensions:	No data
Hp:	*Rpm:* *Psi:*
Service:	Gas compressor drive

With the absorption of small uneconomic country undertakings, high pressure distribution was necessary from the central plant, and this was one of the early sets. These were able to compress to 5 p.s.i. or more, so allowing small mains to carry large amounts of gas and to serve several areas from one unit, from high pressure mains. They ran at some 400 r.p.m., and this was followed by three more, the latest being installed in 1950. The diesel units followed this. The steam sets were still operable in 1967, and used as long as coal gas making continues i.e.1969 or later.

41) Bath, Bath Gas Works — SER 1322i

Type:	Horizontal single cylinder condensing
Photo taken:	1967
Maker & Date:	Bryan Donkin & Co., Chesterfield. Date unknown
Cylinder/dimensions:	16in x 3ft 6in approx
Hp: 20	*Rpm:* 15–20 *Psi:* 100
Service:	Beale type booster drive. One on each side of the engine

These are typical gas booster sets, with casings about 4 feet in diameter, and each would displace some 150,000 cubic feet of gas per hour for local low pressure services. Many of these were later altered with new cylinders and boosters, as gas demands increased with new housing. All of these photographs were taken in 1967 before sea–borne natural gas supplies replaced home–produced coal gas.

42) Bath, Bath Gas Works — SER 1322j

Type:	Diesel engine and compressor
Photo taken:	1967
Maker & Date:	Belliss & Morcom, Birmingham
Cylinder/dimensions:	Gas cylinders $16^{3}/_{4}$in x $6^{1}/_{2}$in
Hp: 335	*Rpm:* 750 *Psi:*
Service:	Long distance high pressure gas supply, by three cylinder semi–radial compressors

The diesel engines were grouped together at one point, to deal with the long distance services needing up to 30 psi to send the gas over great distances, as it was intended finally to have gas supplied only from Plymouth and Avonmouth for the entire West Country. This required pressures up to 30 psi, which needed and was provided by piston type compressors such as these. The compressors were three cylinder units as seen at the right hand side, with a vertical central cylinder flanked by two others at an angle of 45 degrees to the vertical one. The speed was too great and there were frequent difficulties with them.

43) Bath, Isaac Carr & Co., Weston & Twerton Mills, Twerton SER 30a

Type:	Single cylinder beam engine
Photo taken:	1935
Maker & Date:	Unknown. c 1840?
Cylinder/dimensions:	30in x 6ft 0in – Slide valve
	Beam 18ft 0in long. Flywheel 21ft 0in diameter
Hp: 80	*Rpm:* 27 *Psi:* 30
Service:	Woollen cloth manufacture. Water mill with turbines in later years

The above was at the Weston Island Mill which comprised spinning and weaving sections. The 4 floor spinning mill was about 120ft away from the engine house and was driven by an underground shaft which passed under the mill yard to the vertical shaft for the 4 floors. The weaving shed was at one side, and also driven from the underground shaft by bevel wheels and a short vertical shaft to the shed mainshaft The two water turbines were coupled to the beam engine drive by a train of four bevel wheels with the underground shaft driven from one of these. It was a unique layout in that the whole of the gearing was bevel wheels, 12 pairs in all. The Twerton Mill was the finishing section with horizontal tandem Corliss engine and two water turbines. The whole was reorganized in 1937, when a Belliss compound engine and generator of 250 kw capacity was fitted in the Twerton Mill. This drove Twerton by motors and also a considerable part of Weston Island Mill, by a power cable which passed down the river bank to it. The water turbines there were retained however, and assisted to drive Weston Island until the closure.

44) Bath, Brass Mill Lane (on Dutch Island)   SER 30b

Type:	Two undershot waterwheels
Photo taken:	1935
Maker & Date:	Unknown
Cylinder/dimensions:	16ft 0in diameter x 3ft 3in wide
Service:	Rag tearing mill in later years

Water power was used at the brassworks on this site operated by Nicholas de Graef from 1667 until his decease in 1743. The wheels were very similar to those in the Keynsham Mills, and there had been a third wheel, whilst there were also remains of annealing ovens on the site. Nicholas de Graef brought over his own men, starting at the beginning of the English brass battery trade, and the site is marked as a brass mill on Thorpe's map of five miles around Bath of 1742, and probably continued as such, finally coming under the Harford and Bristol Co., but although the site was still known as Dutch Island in the 1930s, there is no record of when brass working ceased. The two water wheels were in regular use in the 1930s, tearing old cloth possibly for shoddy cloth, or else papermaking. The old house dated 1667, and the whole of the buildings have been removed in the flood relief schemes of recent years.

45) Bath, Mr Bowler, Engineer   SER 1323

Type:	Single cylinder horizontal town gas engine
Photo taken:	1967
Maker & Date:	C. Griffin & Co., Bath, about 1880
Cylinder/dimensions:	About 7ft x 1ft 0in – four stroke cycle
Hp: About 6	*Rpm:* 200 *Psi:*
Service:	Drove workshop machinery by belt. Preserved in Bristol Museum

Mr. Griffin was a good engineer who started business in Bath in the 1860s, making agricultural and general machinery and doing repair work. Seeing the need for power with the use

of steam plant, he turned from making small engines and boilers, which he exhibited at the Bath and West agricultural shows, and started making gas engines about 1871, and continuing his development, took out some 17 patents by the turn of the century for gas and oil engines. One of these was for a six stroke cycle, i.e. with one power stroke in three revolutions, and development and manufacture of gas and oil continued until the mid 1920s. There were four gas engines at Mr. Bowler's, one of which had driven the mineral water plant, and the one shown in the print drove a section of the engineers' machinery. A really early design it incorporates several Griffin patents, i.e. for the flame ignition within the flat slide valve at the right hand side, which has a spring loaded pressure plate, and the exhaust valve is driven by a face cam. The design is extremely simple, and readily made with limited equipment.

46) Bath, Stothert & Pitt   SER 244

Type:	Four column beam
Photo taken:	1938
Maker & Date:	Stothert & Pitt, Bath, 1866
Cylinder/dimensions:	12in x 1ft 6in – Slide valve
	Beam 4ft 2in long. Flywheel 6ft 0in diameter
Service:	Preserved at makers' works

The brass plate on this engine states that: *Stothert & Pitt built many engines of this type. This was exhibited in the Exhibition of 1866.* After many years of work, it was purchased back, refinished probably as it was exhibited, and after some years on show in the works yard, is now under cover in the works. It is a very sturdy design, that gave trouble free service. The false cover over the cylinder top, and the complex cylinder casting are fine foundry work.

47) Bath, The Pump Rooms   SER 333

Type:	Two vertical single cylinder engines		
Photo taken:	1946		
Maker & Date:	S. Owen, London? c.1850?		
Cylinder/dimensions:	9in x 1ft 3in – Slide valve		
	Crankshaft 6ft from floor. Flywheel 5ft 8in diameter		
Hp: 2–3	*Rpm:* 35	*Psi:* 60	
Service:	Mineral water pumps. 1 plunger pump per engine off tail rod. 9in plunger, 6 gallons per revolution		

These were situated in the laundry boiler house, side by side, and with the pumps in the basement. One was used at a time, the duty being to pump mineral water up to the hospital for medicinal purposes. There were also two horizontal pumps by Evans but these were little used. All of the exhaust steam went to the calorifiers, for the hot water supply. Upon the scrapping of the engines this steam had still to be supplied directly from the boilers.

48) Bathampton, Sawmill, nr Station   SER 1209

Type:	Double cylinder portable	
Photo taken:	1965	
Maker & Date:	Marshall Sons & Co., Gainsborough, 1874	
Cylinder/dimensions:	10in x 1ft 3in – Slide valves	
Hp: 12	*Rpm:* 120	*Psi:* 80
Service:	Drive for rack saw bench, 9in belt. Possibly owned by Great Western Railway Co.	

The engine and boiler were supplied to the West Cornwall Railway in 1874, but the date of removal to Bath is unknown. The makers advised that the original boiler was condemned, and a replacement No. 39815 was dispatched from Gainsborough in October 1903. It was used at Bath for cutting old railway sleepers into firewood, driving a 36in rack saw–bench by belt from the flywheel. The second boiler again became unsound in the late 1940s, and was replaced by a vertical centre flue crane type boiler, probably made at Swindon works, which supplied steam to the original engine on the locomotive boiler. The plant was disused by 1965, and possibly had only had seasonal use for some years. It was later disposed of, the engine and locomotive boiler being preserved by Mr. Huish at Weston–Super–Mare.

49) Bathford, Bathford Paper Mills   SER 1458a

Type:	Lumb's full governing system
Photo taken:	1973
Maker & Date:	James Lumb & Co., Elland, 1920s
Cylinder/dimensions:	No applicable data
Service:	Engine speed regulation

Lumb's governing system was noted for its exact speed regulation, and this example also embraced the high and low speed safety knock–off fitting, and the distant control which allowed the engine to be stopped from within the factory, so giving even speed and safety. Mechanically it was simple, without dashpots or springs, but with a heavy double conical weight on the spindle which, with the high speed of rotation made it very powerful. The special feature of the system was that the reach rod, by which the governor action was transmitted to the valve gear was varied in length, so that the point at which the steam was cut off was varied in relation to the speed. This was effected by joining the reach rod in the middle with a right and left hand threaded central section, which was turned by the bevel wheels in the middle. The rotation of the bevel wheels was operated by the "putting on and taking off" motion (see SER 1458b) of pawls and ratchet wheel, which by altering the length of the reach rod, varied the speed at which steam was cut–off for a constant governor height. Lumb's governors were things one fitted and forgot, the engine was well cared for in all speed and safety factors.

50) Bathford, Bathford Paper Mills   SER 1458b

Type:	Cut–off ratio attachment
Photo taken:	1973
Maker & Date:	James Lumb & Co., Elland
Cylinder/dimensions:	No other data
Service:	Engine speed regulation

This is the "putting on and taking off motion" as it was called, its purpose being to vary the length of the right and left hand threaded reach rod at the left. This was joined by the threaded sleeve which could slide on flats through the smaller bevel wheel. The movement was effected by the vertical rod at the extreme right which was reciprocated from the eccentric rod, and oscillated the arm carrying the two pawls which turned the bevel wheel to the right or left by either of the ratchet wheels. The movement was initiated by the needle rod fitted with the pear– shaped weight which was operated by the governor weights. This, through the upper of the two flat rods through which it passed, moved a block between the two ratchet pawls, so raising or lowering the ratchet pawls to engage with the teeth of the ratchet wheels which turned the bevel wheel to the right or left to alter the reach rod length. One ratchet pawl was in line with the nearer ratchet wheel, to turn the bevel wheel anti-clockwise, so altering the length of the reach rod and cut–off independently of the governor weight position.

51) Bathford, Bathford Paper Mills   SER 1143a

Type:	Horizontal single tandem	
Photo taken:	1964	
Maker & Date:	Wood Bros., Sowerby Bridge, 1912	
Cylinder/dimensions:	15in & 30in x 3ft 6in – Corliss valves	
Hp: 400	*Rpm:* 86	*Psi:* 150
Service:	Fine quality paper, for Bibles etc	

This is a very old paper–making site, but the long established business was closed after a bad fire in 1900. The site then lay idle until Mr. Tabb, Senior, bought it, and restarted it

with entirely new plant in 1911. The engine was quoted by Wood Bros. at a very low price, just over £1,000 whereas the nearest tender from any other builder (Newton, Bean and Mitchell) was nearly £400 more, and others higher still, all for a similar sized engine. It was a great bargain, as it ran regularly for 120 hours per week, largely unattended, driving the beater machine shafts for 55 years until motors were installed to drive the beaters.Through its very long service, the main repair was a rebore of the high and low pressure cylinders with new pistons and rings in 1951, and the fitting of a Lumbs governor in 1938, after there had been trouble from irregular speed. It may be preserved in Cornwall.

52) Bathford, Bathford Paper Mills   SER 1143b

Type:	Double cylinder enclosed inverted vertical
Photo taken:	1964
Maker & Date:	Walmsley, Bury. Date unknown
Cylinder/dimensions:	11in x 8in – Piston valves
Hp: 60–70?	*Rpm:* 300 *Psi:* 150
Service:	Paper–making machine drive

The paper–making machine was driven by this engine which exhausted into the drying cylinders of the machine. There are numerous drying cylinders, which are geared together at the wet end by geared rings 6ft diameter at the end, with the dry end similar, but with fewer drums, but that end has the reelers. The whole is primarily driven by the vee belts seen, to an overhead shaft, with continuous vee belts with tension pulleys to maintain the tension. The drives were the very complex layouts inevitable with mechanical drives for many drums, but with the adoption of electrical driving for the beaters, the machine drives were also to be converted to motor driving in 1970.

53) Blagdon, Bristol Waterworks Co., Blagdon Pumping Station   SER 87

Type:	Four Woolf compound beam
Photo taken:	1939
Maker & Date:	Glenfield & Kennedy, Kilmarnock, 1902
Cylinder/dimensions:	21in x 5ft 2in and 34in x 7ft 0in – Drop valves
Hp: About 200 each	*Rpm:* 17 *Psi:* 100
Service:	Pump filtered water to City service reservoirs. $2^1/_2$ million gallons per day each to 240ft head

The consulting engineers were T & C Hawksley, whose name was on the base of the chimney, and the whole scheme was typical of their work. There were two engines in each house, with the boiler house between and behind. The engines were in regular use until 1955, when the electrically driven pumps, of greater capacity, were installed in one house, and the two beams in the other house were retained as exhibits. There was a single bucket and plunger pump to each engine on the crank side of the beam, plunger 21in and the bucket 30in diameter, and 3ft 6in stroke. There was no well.

54) Bridgwater, Bridgwater Gas Works   SER 1373a

Type:	Horizontal single cylinder
Photo taken:	1968
Maker & Date:	Bryan Donkin and Co., Chesterfield. Date unknown
Cylinder/dimensions:	About 10in x 10in – Slide valves
Hp: 6–8	*Rpm:* 106 *Psi:* 100
Service:	Extracted gas from retorts and delivered to purifier and cleaning systems

There were four typical small works Beale type exhausters. The two seen were the larger with two smaller ones in the background. They delivered up to 40,000 cubic feet per hour raising the pressure from minus $3^1/_2$ inches to plus $17^1/_2$ inches water gauge. The usual speed was 80 rpm. They were the standard type met everywhere, the whole plant being very well maintained, and fitted with full automatic oiling to allow long running without supervision. There were two similar engines for driving the coke extraction gear of the retorts by belts. All of the plant was dismantled when coal gas production ceased about 1969, much being sold to collectors.

53

55) Bridgwater, Bridgwater Gas Works   SER 1373b

Type:	Various types
Photo taken:	1968
Maker & Date:	No other data
Service:	Pressure boosting to suburban outer areas

The supply system was remodelled in the 1930s, when horizontal hand–fed retorts were replaced by Woodall vertical semi–continuous gasifiers requiring additional exhaust and boosting units for outlying areas as these ceased to make their own gas and were absorbed into the Bridgwater supply system. The photograph shows in the foreground a de Laval turbine driving a Donkin Rateau fan–type low pressure booster for local service. In the background to the left, and at the back, are three long distance service compressors, all Bryan Donkin make, with twin high pressure piston valve engines, and gas compressors on the top, which, taking gas at 0.4 inch pressure, boost it to $3^{1}/_{2}$ pounds per square inch to increase the capacity of the long distance supply mains. All were non–condensing. The small turbine seen in the front was 7 hp only, running at 29,900 rpm, and geared to the turbo fan. The engines ran at about 400 rpm, to suit the piston type compressors.

56) Bridgwater, Bridgwater Dock, Steam Traversing Bridge   SER 1115a

Type:	Sliding traversing span
Photo taken:	1962
Maker & Date:	Maker unknown, Staffordshire, early 1870s
Cylinder/dimensions:	No other data
Service:	Railway and pedestrian crossing over the River Parrett

The bridge section is about 150 ft long, with 100 ft spanning the river, and a 50 ft counter-balance section, with a section on the North side, which could be moved sideways to allow the main section to be pulled back to allow vessels to pass to the Town Quay. There was never any passage for road vehicles, but the railway section was full carrying capacity. It was probably disused after 1920, when small coasting vessels ceased to use the mud berths, the traffic then going in larger vessels (which could not lie on mud) into the main wet dock nearer the river mouth. Although intended for preservation, it was vandalised in 1970–72. Probably the last bridge of the type in the UK.

57) Bridgwater, Bridgwater Dock, Steam Traversing Bridge   SER 1115b

Type:	Twin cylinder vertical non–condensing	
Photo taken:	1962	
Maker & Date:	Maker unknown, 1870?	
Cylinder/dimensions:	6in x 9in – Slide valves	
Hp: 25	*Rpm:* 120	*Psi:* 100
Service:	Steam operating machinery	

The sideways movement of the northern section which gave space for the movement of the traversing span to clear the river passage was provided by racks below it, moved by pinions on shafts driven by bevel wheels from this engine. The traversing movement of the main bridge span was by chains worked from a winding barrel beneath it, again worked by this engine. There was a single vertical centre flue boiler made by the railway company. Each movement of the engine was controlled by safety interlocks which were coupled both to the signals to prevent locomotive movements when the bridge was operated, and also to prevent the side traversing section and the main bridge movements operations occurring at the same time. The shafts seen at the top of the engine frame were for hand operation, if no steam was available. All of the drive was by a single vertical shaft driven by bevel wheels in the casing at mid level of the framing, which provided for reversing by twin bevel wheels and a central sliding bevel pinion wheel with dog clutches.

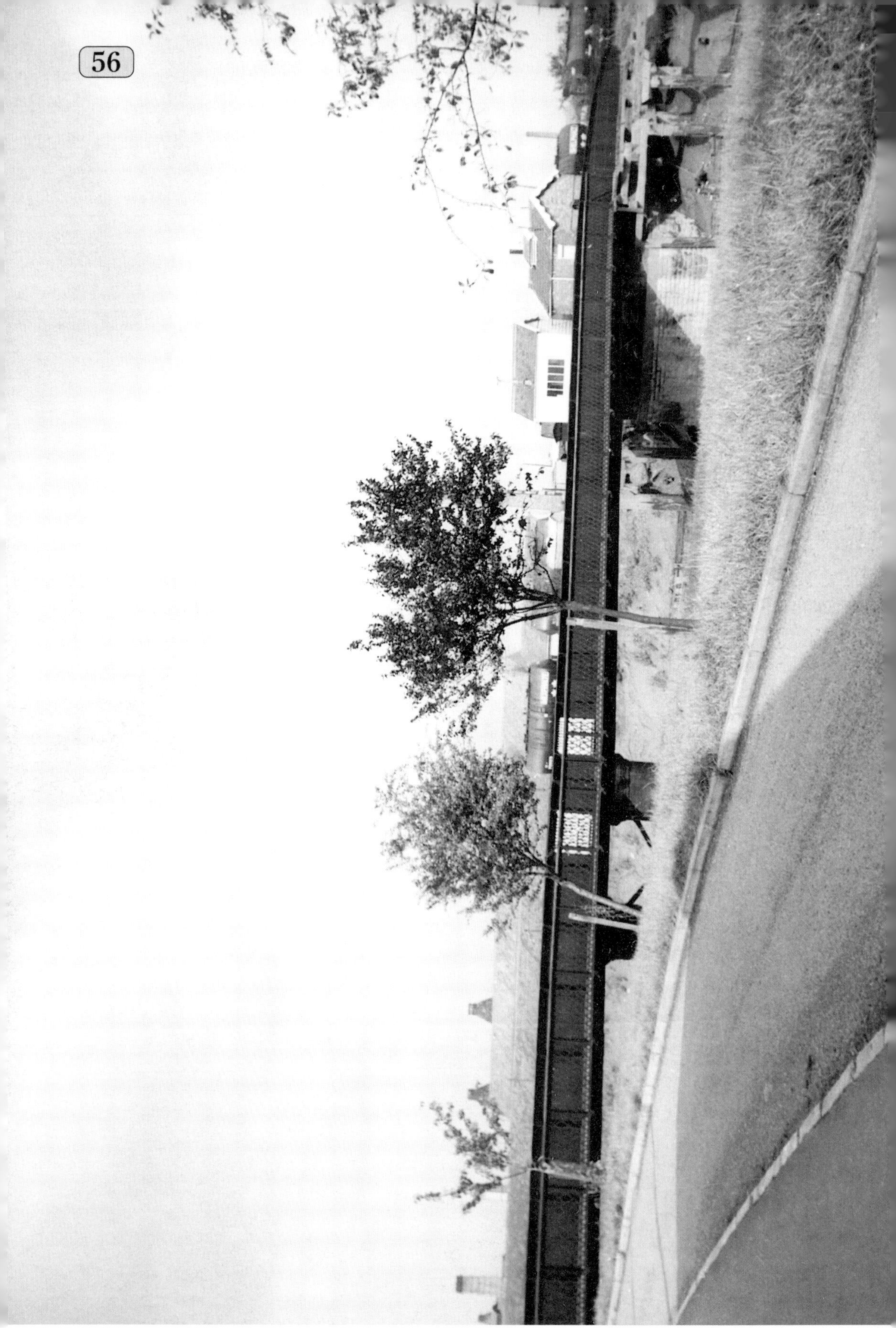

58) Castle Cary, T.S. Donne & Co. SER 399

Type:	Single cylinder horizontal condensing
Photo taken:	1951
Maker & Date:	B. Hick & Sons, 1870s
Cylinder/dimensions:	30in x 4ft 0in – Drop valves
Hp: 120	*Rpm:* 40 *Psi:* 50
Service:	Flax mill drive

There had been a high breast waterwheel at the mill possibly before the engine was installed, probably driving into the same main mill shaft as the engine, with gear and belt drives in the mill. In later years, the drives had been converted to motors with the engine driving a generator from the mainshaft. The engine was an old design with the valves at the side of the cylinder, with variable cut–off altered by a sliding cam. The condenser was below with the air pump driven by a drag link from the crank pin. The engine was scrapped in the 1950s and current taken from the Grid.

59) Chelvey, Bristol Waterworks, Chelvey Pumping Station SER 32a

Type:	Two single cylinder beam engines
Photo taken:	1936
Maker & Date:	Robert Daglish & Co., St Helens, 1866
Cylinder/dimensions:	$31\frac{1}{2}$ in x 6ft 6in – Slide valves
Hp:	*Rpm:* *Psi:*
Service:	City supply, wells to reservoirs. Pump and capacity detail unknown

These engines had long been disused by 1930, although they were probably workable, but no date was available. There was a single pump to each engine placed near to the crank. The pump rods were very stiff, with timber fillers between the webs, which suggests that they were bucket and plunger type working upon the up and downward stroke. The parallel motion, with very short radius rods, was a variant not often met, but they were plain engines that had given good service. They were fitted with Bristows patent anti–friction slide valves, which Daglish's had begun to use in that year; they were in fact their No. 3 and 4 sets of these valves. The connecting rods were at the end of the beam.

60) Chelvey, Bristol Waterworks, Chelvey Pumping Station SER 32b

Type:	Two single cylinder beam engines
Photo taken:	1936
Maker & Date:	James Simpson & Co., Pimlico, 1871
Cylinder/dimensions:	36in x 6ft 0in – Meyer slide valves
	Beam 19ft 0in long. Flywheel 20ft 0in diameter
Hp:	*Rpm:* *Psi:*
Service:	City supply from wells 170ft deep

These were typical Simpson engines, plain and massive, but they differed from Daglish engines in that the pumps on the Simpsons were at the end of the. beam, so overhanging the cranks also the pump rods on the Simpsons were massive circular forgings. An unusual feature was the stiffeners which were bolted over the columns.

61) Chelvey, Bristol Waterworks, Chelvey Pumping Station   SER 32c

Type:	Two Woolf compound beam
Photo taken:	1936
Maker & Date:	J. Watt & Co., 1891
Cylinder/dimensions:	$33^1/_2$ in x 5ft 4in and 52in x 8ft 0in – Drop valves
Hp: 150	*Rpm:* $12^1/_2$ *Psi:* 55
Service:	City supply from wells to Barrow reservoirs. 4,000,000 gallons per day, head about 330ft. 2 well pumps 28in x 2ft 0in. 1 force pump 21in x 8ft 0in

These were probably the last beam engines to leave Watt's works before they closed and although largely superseded by the Lilleshall engine in 1923, they were used until 1945, as long as the water supply permitted. Although plain, the finish was of a high standard throughout, particularly for the valve gear and cylinder and valve chest covers. The main pump rods were at the end of the beams, beyond the cranks, but the well pumps must have been near to the beam centre, unless driven off the main pump rods at the beam end.

62) Chelvey, Bristol Waterworks, Chelvey Pumping Station   SER 32c(2)

Type:	Two Woolf compound beam
Photo taken:	1936
Maker & Date:	J. Watt & Co., 1891
Cylinder/dimensions:	
Hp:	*Rpm:* *Psi:*
Service:	

Watt & Co. later beam engines, where built with drop valves, were fitted with a lay or camshaft, at mid–cylinder level. It was highly finished in every detail, with forged rather than cast iron work everywhere; the cost must have been very high, but to the end it worked silently. Each cylinder had variable cutoff, the HP by the hand wheel at the left, and the LP by the short lever seen above two manual steam valve lifters in the centre of the print.

63) Chelvey, Bristol Waterworks, Chelvey Pumping Station   SER 32c(3)

Type:	Two Woolf compound beam – packing platform
Photo taken:	1936
Maker & Date:	J. Watt & Co., 1891
Cylinder/dimensions:	
Hp:	*Rpm:* *Psi:*
Service:	Town water supply to reservoirs

The same very high finish was maintained throughout: no expense was spared, forgings were used wherever needed, the thickening of the loops of the main and back links for the cotter holes, and the solid forging of the tails for the back links of the parallel motion were all blacksmiths work of a very high order. The cast iron parts however were generally plain, almost the only decoration being upon the entablature cross girders.

64) *Chelvey, Bristol Waterworks, Chelvey Pumping Station* SER 32d

Type:	Inverted vertical triple expansion
Photo taken:	1936
Maker & Date:	The Lilleshall Co., Oakengates, Shropshire, 1923
Cylinder/dimensions:	20in; 35in & 56in x 3ft 6in – Drop valves
Hp: 400	*Rpm:* 22 *Psi:* 160
Service:	City supply from well to reservoirs. 2 Pernis pumps 22in x 3ft 6in in the well. 3 force pumps 17$^5/_8$ x 3ft 6in under the cranks. 3,500,000 gallons per day

This is included here to group all the Chelveys together. It was a standard waterworks triple unit with a ram pump below each crank for the forcing lift to Barrow tanks for the gravity supply to Bristol. The well was at the end of the engine, with the pumps driven from a two throw crank on the other side of the flywheel. This engine was the main pumping unit for over thirty years until electric pumps were installed, but the Watt beam engines remained in use during overhauls as long as steam was used.

65) *Claverton, Kennet & Avon Canal, Claverton Pumping Station* SER 777a

Type:	Waterwheel and geared pumps
Photo taken:	1955
Maker & Date:	1810–13
Cylinder/dimensions:	17ft 6in diameter x 24ft 0in wide
Hp: 26	*Rpm:* 4, pumps 16 *Psi:*
Service:	Water level maintenance. 77,000 gallons per hour to canal 44ft higher

Finished in 1813 after long delay, this was designed by John Rennie, and ran until 1953, when a tooth failure stripped the gearing. The waterwheel was very wide and after repairs by Harveys in 1844, it was altered by the Great Western Railway in the early 1900s when the centre bearing was fitted to make the wheel two halves. It is a flat bucket breast type, using the fall of the River Avon, and now restored by the Kennet and Avon Trust, will be workable in 1973. The whole bucket structure is of timber.

66) *Claverton, Kennet & Avon Canal, Claverton Pumping Station* SER 777b

Type:	Pump drive
Photo taken:	1955
Maker & Date:	
Cylinder/dimensions:	
Hp	*Rpm:* *Psi:*
Service:	

The waterwheel drove by the large gearwheel at the left (on the wheel shaft) with mortise or inserted teeth to a cast iron pinion on the pump driving crankshaft, which has a flywheel. The pumps are at the far end of the building, driven through the cast iron connecting rods and two beams overhead to the 18in diameter bucket pumps.

65

67) Clutton, nr Bristol, Osmond & Co, Sawmills   SER 1393

Type:	Single cylinder portable
Photo taken:	1970
Maker & Date:	Ruston & Hornsby, Lincoln. No 51421, 1916
Cylinder/dimensions:	12in x 1ft 3in approx – Slide valve
Hp: About 20	*Rpm:* 120 *Psi:* 120
Service:	Purchased for auxiliary mill?

This was purchased when disused in 1968 from the Colyton sawmills in Devon, and brought to Clutton on a low loading wagon. It was little used there due to the owner's decease, and was sold with his estate. The Clutton site had been a brickworks, from which much local property was built and the sawmill was started to convert some 70 acres of local timber (mainly oak) for building, using imported timber afterwards. Originally steam driven by shafting under the floors, and firing by scrap timber, a Blackstone oil engine was installed in the early 1920s, and this in turn was replaced by electrical drives in 1938. The plant was kept up to date with new machinery, but all was sold on the owner's decease in 1971.

68) Creech St Michael, Bridgwater & Taunton Canal, Pumping Station   SER 34a

Type:	Cornish type beam
Photo taken:	1936
Maker & Date:	Boulton & Watt, 1827
Cylinder/dimensions:	30in x 7ft 0in
Hp:?	*Spm:* 6–8 *Psi:* 2
Service:	Pumped into canal from River Tone. 1 bucket pump 28in x 7ft 0in stroke

This was very old, having the equilibrium valve at the bottom of the cylinder, as practised before the Cornish design, with only the exhaust at bottom, became general. The practice of putting the exhaust and equilibrium valves together was introduced by Murdock, and this, together with the square section of the equilibrium trunk suggest that it was of the early 1800s date. The boiler was fitted with a gravity water feed, with an escape pipe 8ft 0in high to limit the working pressure to about 2 psi. The water pump was within the engine house. The sectional steam jacket around the cylinder, was another early feature, with its caulked joint between the lower and upper parts.

69) Creech St Michael, Bridgwater & Taunton Canal, Pumping Station   SER 34b

Type:	Cornish beam type
Photo taken:	1936
Maker & Date:	
Cylinder/dimensions:	
Hp:	*Rpm:* *Psi:*

The beam and parallel motion, together with the forged, wrapper type, crosshead fixing were all early design features, and there was no evidence of any alterations. It had long been superseded, by more modern steam, and then electric pumps, since in later years water was supplied to the locomotive feed troughs between the railway lines, as well as to the canal.

70) Flax Bourton & Long Ashton, Barrow & Gatcombe Watermills
SER 318

Type:	Overshot waterwheel
Photo taken:	1945
Maker & Date:	Unknown
Cylinder/dimensions:	14ft x 3ft 9in
Service	Corn milling. Drove 2 pairs 48in stones with an oil engine auxiliary

This mill was rebuilt with the old stones about 1900, and the old style of pit wheel and upright shaft drive retained. The whole was typical of the late modifications made in the traditional mill style, with square cast iron shaft, with hub to suit replacing the early wooden shaft. It was in use in the 1950s.

71) Frome, Frome Water Co., Egford Pumping Station   SER 86

Type:	Two single cylinder beam engines	
Photo taken:	1934	
Maker & Date:	Benjamin Goodfellow & Co., Hyde, Manchester, 1879	
Cylinder/dimensions:	21in x 3ft 0in – Meyer slide valves	
	Beams 11ft 0in long. Flywheels 9ft 6in diameter	
Hp: ?	*Rpm:* 36	*Psi:* 60–80
Service:	Town water supply. Pumps driven from beams.	
	New boiler 1933 100psi	

These were originally arranged to work coupled together if necessary by flanges. The engines had considerable use however, and latterly bearing wear made this impossible. The single fluted columns and general neat design was attractive, but the growth in demand for water led to the installation of a duplex direct acting triple expansion set, but steam was little used after the electric pumps were installed in 1933-4.

72) Glastonbury, England's Mill   SER 6

Type:	Single cylinder A-frame beam non–condensing	
Photo taken:	1932	
Maker & Date:	Unknown	
Cylinder/dimensions:	8in x 1ft 6in stroke	
	Beams 5ft 0in long. Flywheel 7ft 0in diameter	
Hp:	*Rpm:*	*Psi:*
Service:	Flour mill. 2 pairs of 48in stones	

A plain engine, almost the only ornament being neat ribs cast on the cylinder and valve chest. The crosshead worked in guide bars attached to a flange on the top of the cylinder, and the drive was direct from the crankshaft with bevel gears to drive the stones. There was too a horizontal engine also driving two pairs of stones, one by bevel gears and the other by a belt. Two Cornish boilers were installed with cast iron fronts by Sparrows of Martock; but the maker of the boilers was unknown.

73) Highbridge, N.D. Buncombe, contractors   SER 537

Type:	Tandem quick reverse roller
Photo taken:	1953
Maker & Date:	Aveling and Porter, Rochester. No 7411
Cylinder/dimensions:	No data
Hp:	*Rpm:* *Psi:*
Service:	Asphalt rolling

This was a rare design with locomotive boiler and single reduction bevel gear drive to rear roll. Plain slide valve twin cylinder engine, with valves driven from a lay–shaft with spiral sleeve reversing gear, i.e. there was a single eccentric only for each cylinder, providing very fast reversing. The rolls were 3ft 6in. diameter and 4ft wide, and it was in regular use in the 1950s, and probably sold for preservation. The concern owned many steam rollers at the time, but these were less used and disposed of later.

74) Keynsham, Gould Thomas & Co., Albert Mills   SER 297a

Type:	Waterwheel, breast bucket type
Photo taken:	1941
Maker & Date:	Unknown, c.1850?
Cylinder/dimensions:	19ft 0in diameter x 9ft 0in wide
Hp:	*Rpm:* *Psi:*
Service:	Produced dyes from imported timbers

This wheel drove the chipper, which shredded the logs, by feeding them endwise to cutters on the face of the cutter wheels There was another inside the mills which drove the edge runners which pulverised the chips and a rasper for the customers which required finer shredding. The premises had been in various trades, possibly brass, copper and paper. The colour mill started in the 1850s, the first logwood being imported in 1858, and the last in 1948, all supplied by the same importer.

75) Keynsham, Gould Thomas & Co., Albert Mills   SER 297b

Type:	Horizontal single cylinder
Photo taken:	1941
Maker & Date:	Cox & Wilson, Oldbury, Staffs, c.1860?
Cylinder/dimensions:	15in x 2ft 6in – Slide valve
Hp:	*Rpm:* *Psi:*
Service:	Dye production as above

This was a non–condensing engine driving a single pair of edge runner grinding stones, used only when water was short. A plain engine, with the slide valve on the top of the cylinder, it remained unaltered until scrapped about 1952. The wheels were 3ft 0in on the crankshaft, gearing into a mortise toothed wheel 8ft 0in diameter on the mill shaft.

76) Keynsham, Keynsham Brass Mills, Lower Mill   SER 299a

Type:	Entries for 8 undershot water–wheels
Photo taken:	1941
Maker & Date:	Unknown
Cylinder/dimensions:	16–18ft 0in diameter
Hp:	*Rpm:* *Psi:*
Service:	Brass making from raw material and brass made into wire and sheet

View is from the upstream side with entries for the 8 wheels, which closed the whole flow of the River Avon. The right hand section covered with ivy, contained wheels No. 6 to 8, the latter being the wire rolling wheel, driving the rounding rolls to make flat strip into a rough wire; 6 and 7 were wire drawing and charcoal crushing. The left hand part contained the tool grinding wheel, and under the gallery were the 3 rolling mill wheels, two for the heavy sheet rolls, one for a lighter set, and one large one to drive the rumple or heavy wire drawing and the lighter drawbenches on the upper floor. There was not, in fact could not be, any steam auxiliary driving here, but the Top Shop was steam drive only.

77) Keynsham, Keynsham Brass Mills, Lower Mill   SER 299b

Type:	No 4 & 5 waterwheels
Photo taken:	1941
Maker & Date:	
Cylinder/dimensions:	No.4 = 17ft 0in x 2ft 9in
	No.5 = 17ft 0in x 3ft 9in
Hp:	*Rpm:* *Psi:*
Service:	Rolling mill and wire drawing drives

No. 4 drove one of the rolls of the heavy rolling mill, breaking the latten down to a thick sheet, each roll having its own waterwheel. No.5 which was the right hand one was the main wiredrawing one, driving the heavy blocks on the ground floor, and the light ones on the upper floor, by a vertical shaft. All machinery had been removed by 1941, although the waterwheels were still in place. The buildings were very derelict, only ground floor access being allowed by Messrs. Robinson, then the owners.

78) Keynsham, Valley Colour Mills   SER 296

Type:	Waterwheels
Photo taken:	1941
Maker & Date:	
Cylinder/dimensions:	about 15ft x 2ft 0in
Hp:	*Rpm:* *Psi:*
Service:	Colour grinding. Wet and dry pan mills, ball mills and pump

This was probably the Spring Lane brass mill with two wheels at one time, but later was Evens's colour mill. There was also a portable engine to assist the water power, but the boiler of this had failed, and a large vertical boiler was used to steam it. As a brass mill there were probably two battery hammers, but the date of closure was not known, and it was probably a colour mill for over 50 years until it was closed. There had been a third wheel at one time, but this was small, for grinding the tools, and the hammer–head faces.

79) Keynsham, Valley Colour Mills   SER 301

Type:	Undershot waterwheel
Photo taken:	1941
Maker & Date:	Unknown
Cylinder/dimensions:	17ft 0in x 1ft 9in
Hp:	*Rpm:* *Psi:*
Service:	Colour grinding

This was an old waterpower site, where brass, and probably copper working had been done for nearly two centuries. There had been two heavy wheels, with a small one for tool grinding, and the colour mills had also an auxiliary steam drive. This was a portable engine, double cylinder, of which the boiler was condemned, so another vertical one was installed to drive the engine, which remained on the old boiler. The colour plant was extensive, and must have needed frequent assistance from the engine. The wheel and the buildings were typical of the brass trade.
[Note. The notebook entries do not mention the portable engine at all and also record that the site made abrasives for glass paper. APW]

80) Midsomer Norton, Wheeler & Gregory   SER 408

Type:	Single crank compound
Photo taken:	1951
Maker & Date:	Charles Burrell & Co, Thetford. No. 2467, 1902
Cylinder/dimensions:	Sizes unknown. Weight 12 tons
Hp:	*Rpm:* *Psi:*
Service:	Road roller

This was the standard Burrell single crank compound, and in very good condition in 1948, when it was rolling in West Town Lane, Avonmouth. The boiler was allowed 150psi working pressure, but its subsequent history is not known.

81) North Petherton, Somerset Rivers Board, Northmoor
Pumping Station   SER 88

Type:	Vertical twin cylinder condensing
Photo taken:	1934
Maker & Date:	Eastons, Amos & Anderson, 1867
Cylinder/dimensions:	$19^{1}/_{2}$ in x 2ft 3in – Slide valves
Hp: 60?	*Rpm:* 47 *Psi:* 70
Service:	Land drainage. 3,000 acres

This was the standard Easton's drainage engine, of which there were a number in Somerset and the Eastern Counties land drainage systems. They were fitted with expansion cut–off valves for economy, as water levels varied, and were the virtually standard A – frame design with parallel motion guiding for the crosshead, with the air pump driven off the main motion beam. Two new Lancashire boilers were installed in 1913. It was not worked after 1941, when the station had diesel pumps installed and was retained as standby until about 1960.

82) Othery, Somerset Rivers Board, Aller Moor Pumping Station SER 92a

Type:	Vertical twin cylinder non–condensing
Photo taken:	1935
Maker & Date:	Eastons, Amos & Anderson, 1869
Cylinder/dimensions:	13^1/$_2$ in x 2ft 0in – Meyer slide valves
	Crankshaft 6ft 6in from the floor to the centre
Hp: 75	*Rpm: 48–50* *Psi: 60*
Service:	Land drainage. 1926 acres. Centrifugal pump below.
	Vertical shaft and bevel wheel drive

There were several interesting variations to Easton's usual practice at Aller Moor. First the engine was fitted with guide bars, not the usual parallel motion. Also it had a cast iron disc crank (most had a half crank), whilst it was built without a condenser. A remarkable feature was that there was no auxiliary boiler feed unit, there was only a single engine driven feed pump. Another interesting point was that the boiler had a top feed water inlet; this presumably had been fitted to the original boiler and was continued with the Thompson one of 1924.

83) Othery, Somerset Rivers Board, Aller Moor Pumping Station SER 92a

Type:	Engines noted as SER 89 & SER 91 in series
Photo taken:	1935
Maker & Date:	
Cylinder/makers:	
Hp:	*Rpm:* *Psi:*
Service:	Preserved as exhibits

The two engines were removed to Aller Moor site when they were superseded, so that there are now 5 of the 8 engines installed by Eastons in the 1860s now saved. They are the finest set of Easton's engines remaining,and the whole is a tribute to the Board and their then chief engineer Mr Kelting, and their responsible attitude, as there is little left of Easton's great output.

84) Othery, Somerset Rivers Board, Aller Moor Pumping Station SER 92b

Type:	Drainage Station Buildings
Photo taken:	1935
Maker & Date:	
Cylinder/dimensions:	
Hp:	*Rpm:* *Psi:*
Service:	

The drainage station buildings were a neat complex, of local materials. The marl bricks with some stone and the local tiles matched the surroundings. An interesting point was that the chimney was built in the boiler house, without any stone in the cap or corbels. It had very little repair in nearly a century of work.

85) Othery, Somerset Rivers Board, Southlake Pumping Station SER 91

Type:	Inverted vertical twin cylinder non–condensing
Photo taken:	1935
Maker & Date:	Eastons, Amos & Anderson, 1869
Cylinder/dimensions:	10in x 1ft 3in – Meyer slide valve
Hp: 50	*Rpm:* 100 *Psi:* 40
Service:	Land drainage, 500 acres. Centrifugal pump on engine crankshaft

The earlier steam land drainage pumps were usually set at a low level, or drowned, with the engine placed on the surface above, driving the pump by a vertical shaft and bevel wheels, the whole being mounted upon a cast iron well casing, but at Southlake the engine and the pumps were coupled directly together, the whole being placed in a water tight chamber. It was probably the only example of this used in the steam era in Somerset.

86) Paulton, Old Mills Colliery SER 31

Type:	Cornish beam pump
Photo Taken:	1936
Maker & Date:	Wm. Evans & Co., Paulton Foundry, 1842
Cylinder/dimensions:	40in x 8ft 0in
Hp:	*Rpm:* *Psi:*
Service:	Main pump for the colliery

This was the only shaft pump at the colliery and probably had few major repairs until 1937, when a new piston rod, etc, was fitted, after which it ran until nationalisation. It worked on the Cornish cycle, but the steam and equilibrium valves were in line with the beam not across the engine as in Cornwall, with the air plunger type cataract at mid–cylinder level. This was at the older shaft, the later one with its winder by William Evans was dated 1861, and was on the other side of the road.
See SER 1211, for details of this winding engine.

87) Paulton, Old Mills Colliery SER 1211

Type:	Horizontal double cylinder
Photo Taken:	1965
Maker & Date:	Wm. Evans & Co., Paulton Foundry, 1861
Cylinder/dimensions:	About 25in x 5ft 0in – Slide valves
Hp:?	*Rpm:* 28 *Psi:* 60
Service:	Coal winding. Second shaft

This was almost unaltered in a century of use, latterly as a second or escape shaft winder. One possible alteration was that piston tail rods may have been fitted after it was built, since Evans engines do not appear to have had them as a rule, but if so they had certainly been removed at Old Mills and the glands blanked off. The design was certainly of the earliest for horizontal engines, with light open type eccentric rods, slide valves on the top of the cylinders, and cast iron square crankshaft and drum sides. It is preserved by Bristol Museum. The driver worked upon a high level platform above the drum, as at several collieries in the Bristol area; in other areas, the driver usually sat at the side.

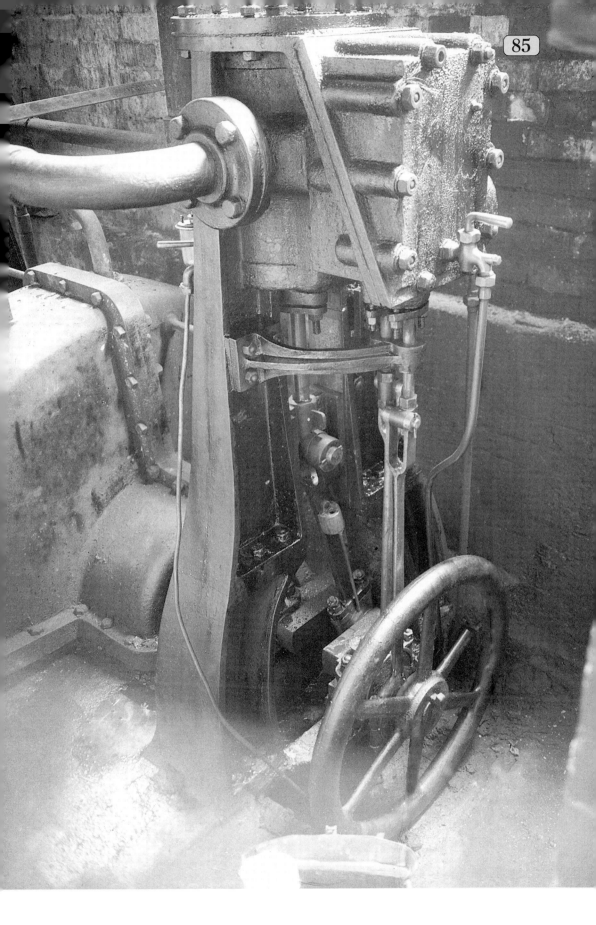

88) Portbury, The Watermill, nr Windmill Hill   SER 29

Type:	High breast waterwheel
Photo taken:	1935
Maker & Date:	Unknown
Cylinder/dimensions:	29ft 6in diameter x 2ft 0in wide
Hp:	Rpm: Psi:
Service:	Flour Mill. 2 pairs of 48in stones.
	Spur ring drive 24ft diameter on side of wheel drove pinion 2ft 4in on the mill shaft with bevels drives to stones

108 buckets in all, i.e.12 segments with 9 buckets in each. Gear teeth 5in wide x $2^1/_2$in pitch. Mainshaft to stones 5in diameter. The stones were driven by a Fairbairn type drive with cast iron toothed bevel wheels. The stones were made by Whitakers, millstone makers, Bristol.

89) Radstock, Kilmersdon Colliery   SER 1225

Type:	Horizontal double cylinder non–condensing
Photo taken:	1965
Maker & Date:	Wm. Evans & Co., Paulton Foundry, 1875
Cylinder/dimensions:	25in x 5ft 0in – Slide valves
Hp: ?	*Rpm:* 28 *Psi:* 60
Service:	Coal winding. Shaft depth not known. Winding drum 12ft 6in x 6ft 0in wide

This was almost identical to the Old Mills engine made 14 years before, and suggests that Evans did not alter their patterns. There was no need to, anyway, as the engines were very good, working hard for up to a century as long as they could cope with the coal drawing needs. This was certainly in regular use as the second shaft engine for over eighty years. The slide valves again were on the top of the cylinders, with the same reversing gear as Old Mills, in which the valve rod links and not the link itself is moved, and with the link fixed to the valve rod end. There did not appear to have ever been tail piston rods fitted to this engine. It was superseded by an electric winder in 1965, when photographed, and scrapped soon after. This also was controlled from a high level platform or pulpit.

90) Radstock, Writhlington Colliery   SER 1210

Type:	Horizontal double cylinder
Photo taken:	1965
Maker & Date:	J D Leigh, Patricroft, Manchester. About 1890
Cylinder/dimensions:	28in x 4ft 6in – Slide valves
Hp: ?	*Rpm:* 35 *Psi:* 80
Service:	Coal winding. Shaft 500 yards deep

The original engine was probably made by Evans of Paulton Foundry; it seems certain that this engine was secondhand from an unknown source. It was larger than many of the winders in the area and with a 22ft diameter drum, wound about 2 tons of coal with 39 revolutions of the drum per trip. The colliery was modernised considerably in the 1960s, and with plough coal cutting was producing nearly 800 tons per shift with 250 men. The coal was sent to Portishead Power Station, but when the demand for coal ceased as oil firing was adopted, the main demand was lost and the colliery was closed, but electrical winding plant had been installed some years before.

91) *Saltford, Harford & Bristol Brass Co., Saltford Mill*   SER 302a

Type:	Six undershot waterwheels
Photo taken:	1941
Maker & Date:	Unknown
Cylinder/dimensions:	About 15ft 0in x 3ft 0in
Hp:	*Rpm:* *Psi:*
Service:	Brass pan hammers, latterly sheet rolling

There was a brass mill here on Thorne's map of 1742, but there was also a paper mill nearby then. In later years, particularly under Bates, the battery trade was extensive but it fell off after the 1880s when brass coated steel was introduced in the Midlands. An attempt was made to use a hammer design from another area, probably when one of the three or more old ones failed. The new one was a total failure, possibly due to poor foundations, and was little used. Only rolling was said to be done after 1890, probably using the heavy gauge sheet ($1/4$ in thick?), from the main mill at Keynsham.

92) *Saltford, Harford & Bristol Brass Co., Saltford Mill*   SER 302b

Type:	Undershot waterwheel
Photo taken:	1941
Maker & Date:	Unknown
Cylinder/dimensions:	9ft 0in x 2ft 0in?
Hp:	*Rpm:* *Psi:*
Service:	Tool grinding. Grindstone on wheel axle

Working thin soft brass required that the tools, particularly the hammer faces, be very true and flat on the face to avoid cutting into the metal. A grinding wheel was therefore provided at each works, so that the tool faces could be maintained on the site. The power needed was slight, therefore a small wheel with single starts for the paddles sufficed. The diameter of the wheels was kept small to increase the speed of rotation, avoiding the use of gearing to give the grindstone high speed.

93) *Saltford, Harford & Bristol Brass Co., Saltford Mill*   SER 302c

Type:	Coal fired annealing oven
Photo taken:	1942
Maker & Date:	Unknown
Cylinder/dimensions:	
Hp:	*Rpm:* *Psi:*
Service:	Sheet annealing

Although Keynsham brass was some of the most ductile in the trade, it work-hardened as rapidly as other brass did under the hammering and rolling, and at some stages had to be annealed at every pass through the tools. The ovens were thus an essential part of each of the works, and there were two pairs at Saltford, which must have been in constant use. The sheets were loaded upon trollies vertically, and wheeled into the centre aperture, the floors comprising iron plates. The fires were at the sides so that the heat came over the top, around the sheets, and to the chimney stalk. The sheets were separated by small slips of metal to allow the heat to pass between them.

94) *Saltford, Harford & Bristol Brass Co., Saltford Mill*   SER 302d

Type:	Works tools and brass pan
Photo taken:	1942
Cylinder/dimensions:	No data
Service:	Brass battery mill; later sheet rolling

The Saltford mill was long noted for the brass pans which were made for home and export trades, the latter largely for evaporating sea water for salt abroad. A wide range of domestic pans was also made there, and these were hammered out of a single flat sheet. The pan in the print was made thus, there were no joins or soldering at all, and the making of such pans was not only very highly skilled, but arduous and costly since much time was needed, with many annealings to soften the brass as the hollowing was deepened. The salt pans were broad but shallow. The hammer head at the bottom was used in battering out the pans, there being several shapes of head. The metal block with eight holes was a wortle or drawing die for wire drawing, with a deep large lead hole with the small drawing hole at the bottom. It was made of carbon steel, and the hole was closed every time a wire was drawn through it.

95) *Saltford, Taylor's Paint Works*   SER 303

Type:	Undershot waterwheel
Photo taken:	1943
Maker & Date:	Unknown
Cylinder/dimensions:	18ft 0in x 3ft 0in wide
Service:	Paint mixing

This site was marked as a paper mill in Thorpe's map of five miles around Bath 1742, but it possibly became a brass plant. The wheel is similar to the brass mill ones, but this may be due to local patterns, even if (unlikely?) the paper mill did use water power. Nothing was known of the history at the site in 1942, but the type of construction would not be earlier than 1820.

96) *Spaxton, Bridgwater Water Works, Ashford Pumping Station* SER 3

Type:	Two simple house – built beam	
Photo taken:	1931	
Maker & Date:	James Watt & Co., 1879	
Cylinder/dimensions:	$15^{3}/_{4}$in x 3ft 0in – Drop valves	
	Beam 12ft 6in long. Flywheel 11ft 0in diameter	
Hp: ?	*Rpm:* 25	*Psi:* 14 for 50ft head, 20 psi for 90ft head
Service:	Town water supply. 1 plunger pump per engine $8^{1}/_{2}$in diameter x 2ft 6in stroke. 2 Cornish boilers 28ft x 6ft 0in	

Typical small house-built engines with single circular columns and twin flitch cast iron beams. One pump per engine driven off the beam near to the connecting rod by twin rods without parallel motion. The steam valves were at the back, driven off a cross shaft, which was driven from the crankshaft by a side shaft and bevel wheels. The inlet valve cams were moveable to adjust the cut–off point. These engines used 10 tons of coal per week, and were in regular use until about 1920. A horizontal single oil cylinder engine was then installed, with three throw pumps by Hathorn, Davey, and this plant, although it gave some trouble, pumped 20% more water using 0.9 ton of oil per week. The beams were retained as stand–by to the other, until load growth compelled the whole to be replaced in 1937.

97) Stoke St Gregory, Somerset Rivers Board, Stanmoor
Pumping Station   SER 89

Type:	Vee twin crank overhead engine
Photo taken:	1934
Maker & Date:	Easton, Amos & Son, 1864
Cylinder/dimensions:	$10^{1}/_{2}$ in x 1ft 9in
Hp:	*Rpm:* *Psi:*
Service:	Land drainage 790 acres. Centrifugal pump below, drive by vertical shaft and bevel wheels

This plant was of the type developed in the 1850s by Eastons for low lift pumping. It comprised a circular cast iron well framing, to which the pump was fixed at the bottom, with the cylinder unit fixed to a planned surface at the top, i.e. above ground. The engine was usually a twin cylinder vertical type and Stanmoor was probably unique in that it had a single crank only, with the two cylinders inclined upward to it at an angle of about 45 degrees. The air pump for the jet condenser was driven by a crank fitted to the other end of the shaft. A new Cornish boiler by Danks was fitted in 1916, which was set with the furnace tube to one side, a system much used on the Continent and this one was said to be very free steaming.

98) Stoke St Gregory, Somerset Rivers Board, Curry Moor
Pumping Station   SER 94a

Type:	Vertical twin cylinder condensing
Photo taken:	1935
Maker & Date:	Easton, Amos & Son, 1864
Cylinder/dimensions:	20in x 2ft 0in – Meyer slide valves
	Crankshaft 6ft 6in from floor parallel motion beams 4ft 6in long
Hp: 150	*Rpm:* 48–50 *Psi:* 80
Service:	Land drainage 3821 acres. Flood relief = 1800 acres. Turbine pump below. Vertical shaft and bevel drive by 94 mortise teeth wheel on crankshaft to 51 on vertical pump shaft.

A typical Easton's design of the period, this was distinctive for having a separate throttle cock for each cylinder. The cut–off valve eccentric is fixed to the side of the main valve eccentric by a bolt in a slot, and this allows them to be moved independently. The bronze runner of the pump has been removed in the re–erection, and is a casting of a very high standard; approximately 4ft 6in diameter by 1ft 4in wide, it is a single casting much of which is only a little over $^{1}/_{4}$ in thick. The engine is preserved in a new house.

99) Stoke St Gregory, Somerset Rivers Board, Saltmoor
Pumping Station   SER 90

Type:	Horizontal twin cylinder non-condensing
Photo taken:	1934
Maker & Date:	R. Spencer, Bridgwater 1867–70?
Cylinder/dimensions:	$10^{1}/_{2}$ in x 1ft 6in – Slide valve Meyer
Hp: 60	*Rpm:* 50 *Psi:*
Service:	Land drainage 600 acres. Centrifugal pump below driven off vertical shaft by iron herringbone toothed bevel wheels

This was possibly the earliest site in Somerset to have drainage, at least there was an advertisement in the local paper for tenders for plant and house in the 1830s, but I have no evidence that anything came of this proposal. The existing engine was said to have been in

the corner of the engine room at one time, with mortise toothed gearing, but this could have related to an earlier unit? The cast iron teeth were said to have been very noisy. The use of a non–condensing engine was unusual in Somerset land drainage, but the use of a feed water heater in the boiler pump suction pipe line saved some heat, the uncondensed steam going to the chimney.

100) Stratton on the Fosse, New Rock Colliery   SER 1212

Type:	Horizontal double cylinder
Photo:	1965
Maker & Date:	Unknown
Cylinder/dimensions:	26in x 5ft 0in – Slide valves
Hp: ?	*Rpm:* 30 *Psi:* 60
Service:	Coal winding. Shaft 383yds. deep

This was almost certainly the last 5ft. diameter shaft in use in the U.K. although they were once common in the Somerset field. Both of the shafts at New Rock were the same, with a single cage in each, and there was almost certainly an Evans winder here at first. The present engine was secondhand, about 1903–4, but nothing was known of its origin, and it had certainly been greatly altered, as the crosshead slides were below the piston centre line. It is possible that new cylinders were fitted from another winder. This engine ran with a single cage when coal drawing, latterly with 3 decks, with one 10 cwt tub of coal on each. An electric winder was installed about 1960 but the colliery was closed a few years later, and by 1973 all coal drawing will have ceased in Somerset.

101) Taunton, E. & W.C. French, Tannery   SER 243

Type:	Four column beam
Photo:	1938
Maker & Date:	Bury, Curtis & Kennedy, Liverpool, c.1840?
Cylinder/dimensions:	15in x 4ft 0in – Slide valve
	Beam 12ft 0in long. Flywheel 16ft 0in diameter
Hp: ?	*Rpm:* 35 *Psi:* ?
Service:	Works drive, by belt

This is the only remaining mill engine by these makers and had run unaltered for a century. It came to the tannery from an unknown source in the 1890s, and drove the tan pumps and leather finishing machinery by belts. The 4-column framing for the beam centre was cast, together with the bearing pedestals, with the columns. The short fluted decorative section at the top of the connecting rod, and the moulding on the face of the cast iron crank were all features of the pre-1850 designs, as was the built up flywheel with the rim in 6 sectors, joined at each arm. The only known repair over many years was new piston rings. There was one Cornish boiler for 50 psi in 1938, when the beam engine was in regular use. The works converted to motor drive in 1948 and the engine remained in situ in 1968.

102) Taunton, Pearsall's Silk Mills   SER 236

Type:	Woolf compound beam
Photo:	1938
Maker & Date:	Easton & Amos, London, 1850
Cylinder/dimensions:	Unknown
	Beam 10ft 0in long. Flywheel 12ft 0in diameter
Hp:	*Rpm:* 48 *Psi:*
Service:	Factory drive. Spur gear wheels

A small industrial engine with interesting features. The two piece flywheel with oval section rim, and with the gear wheel separate and staked on to the crankshaft were early features, whilst the slight beam, parallel motion details, the globular crosshead and the triangular section eccentric strap were Eastons features of the period. So, too, was the use of flat iron strips between the tails of the mortise teeth of the driving gear wheel, a feature seen on the Eastons drainage engines of the area moors. The absence of an upper floor made the engine room very light; it was usually board floored above. The engine is now preserved in the Castle Museum, Taunton.

103) *Weston–super–Mare, Weston–super–Mare Water Works* SER 289

Type:	Two diagonal compound differential
Photo:	1940
Maker & Date:	Hathorn, Davey & Co., Leeds, 1889
Cylinder/dimensions:	15in & 26in x 2ft 6in – Slide valves
	Disc shaft 8ft 0in from floor
Hp:	*Rpm:* 16–20 *Psi:* 80
Service:	Town supply from surface source. 2 double acting bucket pumps 15in x 2ft 3in delivered to reservoir 1,500yds away

This was the third set of engines in the town supply service and was succeeded by a Sulzer diesel engine and pump about 1925, and again by electric pumps after 1947. The Daveys, together with two new Galloway boilers, and the re–setting of another, cost £3194 and were the main units for over 30 years. The Davey differential engines worked very efficiently, the station engineer, Mr. Burnell being very keen. He made a fine model of one of them, almost the only known model of the diagonal type. This is now on display in Weston–super–Mare Museum.

104) *Weston–super–Mare, Weston–super–Mare Gas Works*   SER 1325

Type:	Two inverted vertical single cylinder
Photo:	1968
Maker & Date:	Bryan Donkin & Co., Chesterfield. Date unknown
Cylinder/dimensions:	18in x 1ft 6in – Slide valves
Hp: About 30 max	*Rpm:* 72 *Psi:* 100
Service:	Gas pressure boosting and exhausting services. New boosters for 250,000 cu.ft. per hour added 1947–50

Weston gas works, like those in other areas, was gradually modernised from 1920, with high speed engines for high pressure distribution to outlying areas taken over. There were, beside the verticals, four small open type horizontal engines for the continuous discharge machinery of the vertical retorts, and other small plant. By the time the works were closed for gas production in 1968, there were two large electric and two steam compressors for long distance, together with several small local service steam and electrically driven sets. The pattern changed greatly on the conversion from a producing to a holder station in 1968, when most of the existing plant was scrapped. As a comparison to these traditional types, a Donkin compound high speed engine for high pressure mains service, probably late 1940s, was fitted with steam cylinders $18^{1}/_{2}$ in and $23^{1}/_{2}$ in x 10in stroke and gas compressor cylinders of 21in bore on the top of the steam cylinders.

105) *Weston–super–Mare, Weston–super–Mare Gas Works*   SER 1325b

Type:	Horizontal single cylinder
Photo:	1968
Maker & Date:	Bryan Donkin & Co., Chesterfield. Date unknown
Cylinder/dimensions:	12in x 1ft 6in – Slide valve
Hp: About 20	*Rpm:* 60 *Psi:* 80
Service:	Water gas pressure boosters

The water gas or producer gas plant had its own exhausters and boosters, which, of the traditional type as seen, may have been transferred from the coal gas side. This was the standard Donkin design, with twin flywheels which gave steadiness when, as usual, they were run very slowly. Full automatic lubrication was provided as the engine ran virtually unattended, with merely periodical checks to see that the oiling was continuing. Several of these engines are now preserved, as the small size made them easy to handle and store.

106) *Westonzoyland, Somerset Rivers Board, Chedzoy Moor* *Pumping Station*   SER 94

Type:	Vertical twin cylinder condensing
Photo:	1935
Maker & Date:	Easton, Amos & Son, 1866
Cylinder/dimensions:	20in & 21³/₄ in x 2ft 0in – Slide valves
Hp: About 150	*Rpm:* 48 *Psi:* 100
Service:	Land drainage 3,000 acres. Centrifugal pump below. Vertical shaft and bevel wheel drive

This was probably the only attempt at staged expansion in the Sedgmoor area. Built as a twin cylinder, one of these was replaced by one as large as could be got in. The area ratio was very narrow, and although each cylinder used the steam in turn, the economy was poor even with the use of steam at 100 psi, the highest pressure used in the drainage engines of the area.

107) *Westonzoyland, Somerset Rivers Board, Westonzoyland* *Pumping Station*   SER 93

Type:	Vertical twin cylinder condensing
Photo:	1935
Maker & Date:	Easton, Amos & Son, 1861
Cylinder/dimensions:	20in? x 2ft 0in – Meyer slide valve
Hp: 120?	*Rpm:* 48–50 *Psi:* 70
Service:	Land drainage 2,000 acres. Centrifugal pump below. Vertical shaft and bevel wheel drive

Again a typical Eastons drainage pumping unit, as widely used from 1850 onwards until the horizontal type predominated in the 1880s. It comprised a pair of vertical engines coupled to the ends of the crankshaft, on which was mounted the large bevel wheel for the pump drive. The whole was supported by neat A-frames, with the cylinders below the floor, with parallel motion for the crosshead guides, and the air pumps driven from the parallel motion beams. An interesting feature was the use of flat steel wedges driven between the tails of the mortise teeth, to retain them in place, instead of metal pins driven into the tails themselves. The boiler was supplied new by Danks of Netherton in 1914 and was standard Lancashire type.

108) *Winford, Winford Red Co.*   SER 1217

Type:	Double cylinder overtype
Photo:	1965
Maker & Date:	Marshall Sons & Co., Gainsborough, 1921
Cylinder/dimensions:	12in and 12in x 1ft 6in – Slide valves
Hp: About 30	*Rpm:*120 *Psi:* 100
Service:	Crushing plant drive. 12in and 18in belt to main shafts

This was believed to have been bought new for a sawmill in Shropshire in 1921 and sold by them in 1932, the date it came to Winford. It had driven crushing and grinding plant, i.e. rotating pan mills and rolls by the 18in belt, and the 12in belt probably drove sifting and screening units. All of the old plant however was completely replaced by modern electrical high speed grinders and sifters in 1960, and most of the old plant except the engine was gone. The engine was a standard unit in all ways, heavily used in its forty years of work, in two concerns whose activities certainly applied great over-loads at times. The Marshall engine was to be preserved by an unknown group.

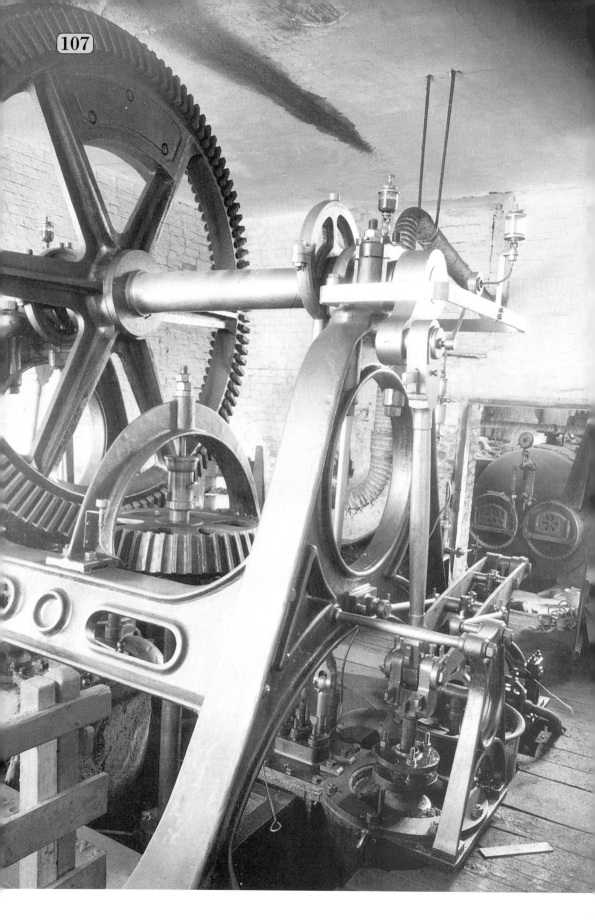

109) Wookey, Hodgkinson, Wookey Hole Paper Mill   SER 478

Type:	Horizontal tandem condensing
Photo:	1952
Maker & Date:	G. K. Stothert, Bristol, 1880s?
Cylinder/dimensions:	About 18in and 32in x 3ft 6in – Slide valves
Hp: 200	*Rpm:* 90 *Psi:* 80
Service:	Drove pulp beating mills

This drove the beater lineshaft by spur gears, of 120 and 52 teeth, one with mortise teeth, 10in wide. It was Stothert's usual plain sound design, but a King's drop cut-off valve was added later under governor control. The crankshaft was 10in. diameter with the massive eccentric 3ft 0in diameter for the air pump drive, between the main bearing and the flywheel. There were none of the usual flat cotters in the design at all, and the spur gearwheel driving the governor and cut-off gear was remarkable for having internal and external teeth upon the same rim, the wheel being overhung on the governor shaft end. It was scrapped in a major reorganization in the 1950s.

110) Yatton, Titan Ladder Co   SER 1498

Type:	Single cylinder oil engine & generator
Photo:	1976
Maker & Date:	Ruston, c.1930
Cylinder/dimensions:	Unknown
Hp: 45	*Rpm:* 300 *Psi:*
Service:	Works drive

The sawmill was old established, and may have had a steam engine at one time, but nothing was known of this. The machines had long been electrically driven, and the Ruston oil engine was installed with an alternator, in the late 1920s, to drive the whole plant. In later years, more current was taken from the Grid as new machines were installed at the same time the engine needed attention to carry the full load, and from about 1975; current supply was taken entirely from the Grid. The engine and generator, still in sound working order, were then offered for sale.

WILTSHIRE

111) Devizes, Wadworth & Co., Brewery   SER 1218

Type:	Horizontal single cylinder non-condensing
Photo:	1965
Maker & Date:	George Adlam & Son, Bristol, c.1900
Cylinder/dimensions:	10in x 1ft 6in – Slide valve
Hp: 25	*Rpm:* 100 *Psi:* 100
Service:	Brewery plant drive

The brewery started about 1860, and possibly was all hand operated until this engine was installed, probably when there were extensions and alterations. There was no record of a previous engine, and the interesting feature of this one is that it is on the first floor, which is only lightly stiffened, although the brick engine bed is 2ft 9in deep. It drove the plant by an 8in belt, and bevel wheels to a vertical shaft, which drove a hoist, and doubtless other plant upstairs, and the well pumps, 90ft deep and now replaced by electric units. The engine was retained although little used in the late 1960s. It was called an *Adlams plant*, as they did much of the maintenance work as well as supplying new units.

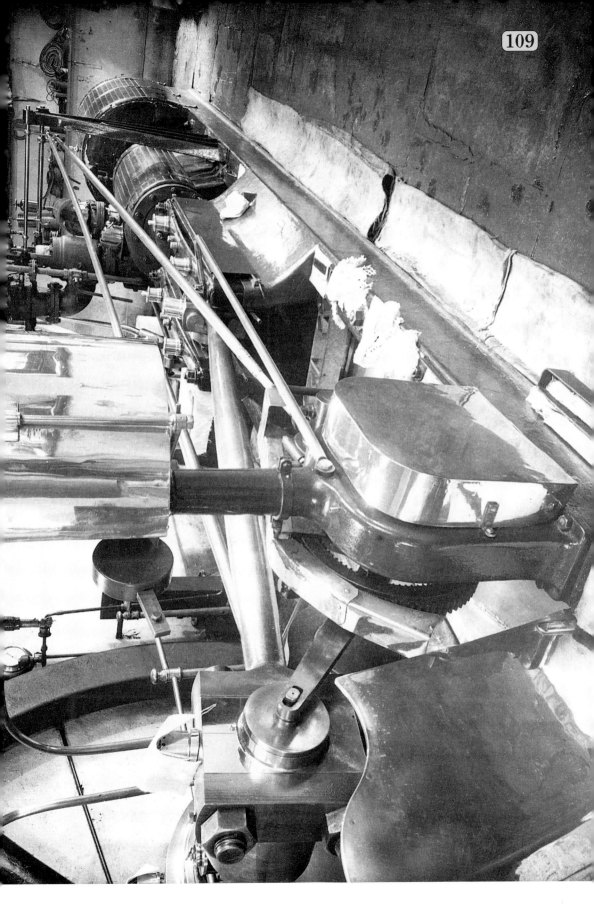

112) East Grafton, Mr Hosier, Farmer   SER 675

Type:	Compound ploughing engine
Photo:	1954
Maker & Date:	J. Fowler & Co., Leeds. Date unknown
Cylinder/dimensions:	About 7½ in and 12in x 1ft 0in – Slide valves
Hp:	*Rpm:* *Psi:*
Service:	Land ploughing

This was the Everitt type, without bevel gearing, the cable drum being carried upon a bracket at the side of the boiler. It was one of a pair which had been greatly used until superseded by tractors in the 1950s. One was gone and the other scrapped by 1960. The ploughing cable was led from the rear of the engine by a horizontal pulley beneath the water tank behind the cab.

113) Great Bedwyn, Kennet & Avon Canal, Crofton Pumping Station   SER 411

Type:	Two non-rotative beam pumps
Photo:	1951
Maker & Date:	Boulton, Watt & Co, 1812 & 1844
Cylinder/dimensions:	No 1 42in x 8ft 0in, 1812
	No 2 do do as altered
Hp: 38-40	*Spm:* 11½ *Psi:* 20
Service:	Maintained canal level

These lifted about 230 gallons per stroke each, and about 1½ million gallons per day when maintaining the canal level, and filling the locomotive water troughs on the main Great Western Railway line. The first engine of 1802 was replaced by a Sims compound in 1844, and the other then altered to the Cornish system. The compound was altered to a 42in single in 1905. The lift was about 40ft 0in and they were in regular use until 1952, and now, restored by the Kennet and Avon Trust, are run under steam at specified times.

114) Swindon, Swindon Gas Works   SER 1324a

Type:	Horizontal gas making retorts
Photo:	1967
Maker & Date:	Jenkins & Co., Retford, Notts
Cylinder/dimensions:	No applicable data
Hp:	*Rpm:* *Psi:*
Service:	Coal gas production

These were almost certainly the last horizontal gas retorts to be installed, i.e. in 1944 and 1947, and equally the last to be used in a major United Kingdom works. There were two main banks of retorts each containing 10 beds of ten retorts each, i.e. some 200 retorts in all. Each was about 22ft long and could hold 15 cwt. of coal per charge. They were mechanically filled by a belt travelling over pulleys at high speed, which threw the coal to the back of the retort. The belt was electrically driven and fitted to a travelling carriage, the coal being supplied from the bunkers (seen overhead) through the hole seen in the sliding plate at the bottom of the hoppers. The coke was discharged by a pusher, again electrically driven, which was operated from the filling end to push out the coke on to a travelling belt at the other end. It was the last traditional retort house, and gas production ceased in March 1968, when all of the plant was dismantled.

113

115) Swindon, Swindon Gas Works   SER 1324b

Type:	Steam & electric engines
Photo:	1968
Maker & Date:	No data
Cylinder/dimensions:	
Hp:	*Rpm:* *Psi:*
Service:	Boosters for distribution service. Roots blowers for local system and piston compressors for long distance services

Although the traditional pattern was retained for the gas production side, the distribution section at Swindon was continual advancing, and from 1939, when a Sissons high speed engine and Roots blower was put in for local distribution, there was a series of similar high speed engines. Some had piston type compressors for high pressure systems, as seen on the right, a Bryan Donkin with the steam cylinders on the top, and at the left a compound by the same makers with the gas cylinders on the top. Two Roots blowers electrically-driven, in the foreground, were for local service. All of this was to be altered when coal gas production ceased. Even before this, however, there were motor driven compressors for the latter services that would fit into the ultimate pattern.

116) Swindon, The Sawmill, Rodbourne Cheney   SER 443

Type:	Compound traction engine
Photo:	1952
Maker & Date:	Ruston Hornsby, No 52370. Date unknown
Cylinder/dimensions:	$4^1/_2$ in and 8in x 9in – Slide valves
Hp:	*Rpm:* *Psi:* 150
Service:	General haulage

This was the standard engine of a late design, but long disused in 1948, and scrapped soon after. It had had very heavy use, the gearing being greatly worn. It was of the four shaft type, with two speeds, and the feed pump driven directly from the crankshaft. There were 28 tubes, $1^3/_4$ in diameter, in the 22in diameter boiler barrel.

117) Trowbridge, McCall Bros   SER 1067

Type:	Horizontal single tandem
Photo:	1961
Maker & Date:	Davey, Paxman, Colchester, 1909
Cylinder/dimensions:	Lentz drop valves
Hp: 750	*Rpm:* *Psi:* 180
Service:	Woollen cloth mills. Electrical drives from alternator

This was one of the two engines installed by J.S. Fry, when they built the No 7, mill in Bristol, to generate electricity for the motor drives which were installed as it was equipped. The two engines were together at the rear of the boiler house of No 7 factory, which started in 1901 and was finally completed in 1911. The boiler house then contained 7 Lancashire and one large Babcock water tube boiler. McCall Brothers purchased the engine for the electrical driving of their mill in 1931 after Fry's closed and moved to Somerdale from 1926. It was in regular use certainly until 1968, when the photograph was taken at Trowbridge.

118) Westbury, Laverton & Co., Cloth Mills   SER 35

Type:	McNaughted single beam
Photo:	1936
Maker & Date:	Possibly Musgrave, 1835?
Cylinder/dimensions:	36in x 7ft 0in?, then new cylinder 48in x 8ft 0in, 1856
	36in x 4ft 0in, McNaught H.P. Musgrave, 1872
	Beam 21ft 0in long. Flywheel 25ft 0in diameter
Service:	Woollen cloth mill. Gear drives to spinning and weaving sections

This appears to be a case where the power soon outgrew the engine since the new cylinder of 1856 with its 8ft 0in stroke was too long for the beam. The standard proportion was for the beam to be three times as long as the stroke, a proportion which gave an easy motion to the engine; this one, with its steep angle of the beam at the end of the stroke, looked odd although it ran well enough to work for over eighty years. In fact it was largely due to metal fatigue that it was superseded. There was undoubtedly water power originally, since Mr. Willoughby in his review of water power in the area indicates six streams in Westbury. The probable date of the first engine suggests the growing use of power weaving and then, the first engine was overloaded needing the larger cylinder by 1856, with the logical procedure of McNaughting when the boilers were worn and the load again increased. The several gear drives suggested that buildings had been added from time to time by a go-ahead firm.

119) Westbury, Westbury Ironworks   SER 37a

Type:	McNaughted single beam
Photo:	1936
Maker & Date:	Unknown. Engine house date, 1857
Cylinder/dimensions:	40in x 7ft 0in – all drop valves
	McNaught high pressure 40in x 3ft 6in. Musgrave, 1873
Service:	Blast furnace blowing engine. Air blowing tub 84in x 7ft 0in. Crank stroke 4ft 0in

This was the usual layout for a blowing engine with the steam and air cylinders at the opposite ends of the beam, with the crankshaft near to the steam cylinder. When McNaughted therefore, the high pressure cylinder was placed between the blowing tub and the beam centre. McNaughted compounding of blowers was rare and it seems likely that the successful results of compounding of Lavertons' engine led to this being done at the ironworks in the following year.

120) Westbury, Westbury Ironworks   SER 37b

Type:	Two long crosshead vertical simple
Photo:	1936
Maker & Date:	W. & J. Galloway, 1905?
Cylinder/dimensions:	38in x 5ft 0in – Piston valve
Service:	Blast furnace blowing engine. Air blowing tub 80in x 5ft 0in

The ironworks were closed about 1900 and were re-opened some three years later by a new company (*Engineering* 20-10-1903), and this pair were put in at the restart. There was also a low-pressure turbine and a horizontal four cylinder gas engine and generator probably of continental make installed not long after this. The works was thus well managed and kept up to date. It was finally closed during the 1930s, and the site cleared about 1940. The iron ore no doubt came from Seend, as well as the Brendon Hill mines. There were 7 gas-fired Lancashire boilers in 1934.

121) *Wilton, E.V. Naish Ltd., Felt Mills*   SER 674

Type:	Horizontal single tandem condensing
Photo:	1954
Maker & Date:	Marsden's Engines, Heckmondwike, 1923
Cylinder/dimensions:	14in and 28in x 3ft 0in – Corliss valves
Hp: About 300	*Rpm:* 80 *Psi:* 150
Service:	Works drive. Electric generator, by ropes from flywheel

This was named *Gladys* and was purchased secondhand from a textile mill when it closed (name and site unknown, but it was in Yorkshire). It was moved and overhauled by Marsden's who were then still in business (1947). The work was extremely well done and the engine was kept very clean. There was, however, trouble over the drive to the generator, and following changes in this, it was decided to take current from the Grid, and the engine was scrapped in the 1950s.

122) *Wootton Bassett, Edwards, Agricultural Engineer*   SER 587

Type:	Single cylinder portable
Photo:	1953
Maker & Date:	Robinson & Auden, Wantage. No. 1328. Date unknown
Cylinder/dimensions:	About 7in x 11in – Slide valve
Hp: 10	*Rpm:* 140 *Psi:* 100
Service:	On hire to farmers, with threshing tackle

This was an uncommon make, but still complete and possibly usable in the 1950s. The cylinder steam jacket was permanent and very effective, and variable cut-off was arranged for by sliding the eccentric across a flange on the crankshaft. It had given good service over many years, but was scrapped about 1960.

ENGINE MAKERS INDEX

Manufacturer	SER No	Plate No
Adlam, G., & Son	1218	111
Allen, W. H.,	1376b	24
Almond, J. P.,	1375	37
Barrett, Exall & Andrewes	1457	16
Bellis & Morcom	1451a	22
	1211	39
	1322b	40
	1322j	42
Boulton, Watt & Co.	34a	68
	34b	69
	411	113
Brown & May	956	7
Bryan Donkin	8a	29
	1322	39
	1322i	41
	1373a	54
	1373b	55
	1325	104
	1325b	105
	1324b	115
Bury, Curtis & Kennedy	243	101
Coalbrookdale Co.	4b	12
Copperhouse Foundry	814	1
Cox & Wilson	297b	75
Dalgish, R., & Co.	32a	59
Davy, Paxman	1067	117

Manufacturer	SER No	Plate No
Easton & Amos	236	102
Easton, Amos & Son	89	97
	94a	98
	94	106
	93	107
Easton, Amos & Anderson	88	81
	92a	82
	92a	83
	91	85
Easton & Anderson	86	30
	231	36
Evans, W., & Co.	31	86
	1211	87
	1225	89
Galloway, W. & J.	37b	120
Gimson & Co.	1425	6
	233a	33
Glenfield & Kennedy	87	53
Goddard, Massey & Warner	957	14
Goodfellow, B., & Co.	86	71
Griffin, C., & Co.	1323	45
Hathorn, Davey & Co.	1377	32
	289	103
Hick, B., & Sons	399	58
Leigh, J. D.,	1210	90
Lilleshall Co.	232	35
	32d	64
Lumb's Governing System	1458a	49
	1458b	50
Marsden's	674	121
Marshall Sons & Co.	1209	48
	1217	108

Manufacturer	SER No	Plate No
Musgrave, J. (?)	35	118
Owen, S.,	333	47
Pollit & Wigzel	1114	3
	1473	38
Scott & Hodgson	672	17
Simpson, James & Co.	1376c	25
	230	26
	32b	60
Spencer, R.,	90	99
Stothert, G. K.,	478	109
Stothert & Pitt	244	46
Tangyes Ltd	1207	19
Thornewill & Warham	956	7
Waller	1322	39
Walmsley	1143b	52
Watt, James & Co.	486	27
	32c	61
	32c (2)	62
	32c (3)	63
	3	96
Willans & Robinson	488a	10
	488b	11
Wood Bros.	1143a	51
Worthington, Simpson & Co.	10b	20
	1376a	23
	233b	34
Wren & Hopkinson	1374	13
Unknown	234a	4
	234b	5
	1451	21
	1378	28

Manufacturer	SER No	Plate No
Unknown	30a	43
	1115a	56
	1115b	57
	6	72
	1212	100
	37a	119

NON STATIONARY ENGINE MAKERS INDEX

	SER No	Plate No
Beer fermenting vats	1459b	9
Brass annealing oven	302c	93
Brass pan	302d	94
California Stamps	1463	2
Drainage Station Buildings	92b	84
Gas Retorts	1324a	114
Oil engine & generator	1498	110
Traction engine	536	15
	535	18
	1393	67
	537	73
	408	80
	443	116
	587	122
Pumps	8c	31
Waterwheels	30b	44
	777a	65
	777b	66
	318	70
	297a	74
	299a	76
	299b	77
	296	78
	301	79
	29	89
	302a	91
	302b	92
	303	95
	675	112
Wortle (wire drawing die)	302d	94

SERIES EDITOR, TONY WOOLRICH

Tony was born in Bristol in 1938. He became interested in technical history in his school days.

He trained as a craftsman in the engineering industry, and from 1970 has combined his craft and historical skills in modelmaking for museums and heritage projects.

He has also published books and articles on aspects of technical history and biography. A particular interest is industrial espionage of the 18th century. Another interest is 18th century and early 19th century technical books and encyclopaedias, in particular Rees's *Cyclopædia*, (1802-1819). He has been working on a biography of the engineer John Farey, jr (1791-1851) for the past 20 years.

Since 1989 he has been heavily involved cataloguing for the National Monuments Record, Swindon, the Watkins Collection on the Stationary Steam Engine. He is also a constant consultee to the Monuments Protection Programme of English Heritage.

Since 1994 he has been acting as a contributor to the New *Dictionary of National Biography* working on biographies of engineers and industrialists. He is a contributor to the *Biographical Dictionary of Civil Engineers,* published by the Institution of Civil Engineers, 2002.

He has recently completed for Wessex Water plc a study of the water supplies of Bridgwater, Wellington (Somerset) and Taunton, and was part of the team setting up the company's education centres at Ashford (near Bridgwater) and Sutton Poyntz (near Weymouth).

 # ACKNOWLEDGEMENTS

Thanks are due to Keith Falconer who had the foresight to acquire the collection for the RCHME, and to Helga Lane, (late of the RCHME Salisbury office) who made the original computer database of the Steam Engine Record.

Much help in the production of these volumes has been given by David Birks, National Monuments Record Archives Administration Officer; Anna Eavis, Head of Enquiry and Research Services, and the members of the public search room staff at Swindon.

Colin Bowden and Jane Woolrich did the often-difficult proof checking.

Many thanks to John Cornwell for providing the photographs of the author.

The series publishes George Watkins's texts as he wrote them and it is acknowledged that he did make mistakes. While obvious spelling and typing errors have been changed, to begin to rewrite his work in the light of present-day knowledge is an impossible task.

The Publisher and Editor welcome constructive comments from readers. Where appropriate, these will be incorporated into volume 10.

LANDMARK COLLECTOR'S LIBRARY

Stationary Steam Engines of Great Britain
The National Photographic Collection

THE VOLUMES:

1   Yorkshire

2   Scotland, Cumberland, Co Durham, & Northumberland

3   Lancashire (two books: Volume 3.1 & 3.2)

4   Wales, Cheshire, Shropshire

5   North Midlands: Derbyshire, Leicestershire, Lincolnshire, Nottinghamshire, Staffordshire

6   South Midlands: Berkshire, Bristol, Buckinghamshire, Gloucestershire, Herefordshire, Hertfordshire, Oxfordshire, Warwickshire, Worcestershire

7   The South and South West: Cornwall, Devon, Dorset, Hampshire, Isle of Wight, Somerset, Wiltshire

8   London & South East: London, Kent, Middlesex, Surrey, Sussex

9   East Anglia: Bedfordshire, Cambridgeshire, Essex, Norfolk, Northants, Suffolk

10 Marine engines (and readers notes)

General Specification for all Volumes

Hardback, sewn binding with a laminated dust jacket. Printed on high quailty paper, size: 246 x 172mm (approx 9.75 x 6.75 inches).

Prices will vary according to length. Volume 1 is the longest book. On some of the smaller volumes, opportunity may be possible to incorporate additional photographs from George Watkins' field note books, which are additional to the main engine record and not generally available. Volume 3 (Lancashire) is split into two parts.

Hardback books on local history which you will enjoy having and dipping into time and again.

Full details upon request

LANDMARK
Publishing Ltd ● ● ●

Ashbourne Hall, Cokayne Ave, Ashbourne, Derbyshire, DE6 1EJ England
Tel 01335 347349   Fax 01335 347303
e-mail landmark@clara.net   web site: www.landmarkpublishing.co.uk

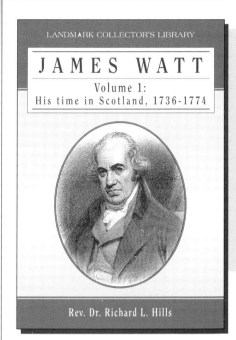

James Watt
Volume 1: His time in Scotland,
1736 - 1774

Rev. Dr. R. L. Hills

ISBN: 1 84306 045 0

Price: £35.00

480pp; hardback; 16pp photographic
section

> *"fastidious in its references, and none the worse for that... destined for a long shelf life"*
>
> (Journal of the Institution of Mechanical Engineers)

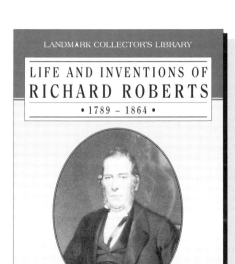

Life and Inventions of Richard Roberts
1789 - 1864

Rev. Dr. R. L. Hills

ISBN: 1 84306 027 2

Price: £29.95

256pp; hardback; 8pp photographic
section

> *"a vivid portrait of one of Manchester's finest industrial minds"*
>
> Rossendale Free Press

LANDMARK
COLLECTOR'S LIBRARY

LANDMARK
Publishing Ltd ●●●

Ashbourne Hall, Cokayne Ave, Ashbourne, Derbyshire, DE6 1EJ England
Tel 01335 347349 Fax 01335 347303
e-mail landmark@clara.net web site: www.landmarkpublishing.co.uk

Mining Histories

- Cheadle Coalfield, Staffordshire, The History of the   *ISBN: 1 84306 013 2, £19.95*
- Churnet Valley Iron, The mills & the mines   *ISBN: 1 84306 011 6, paperback, £9.95*
- Collieries of South Wales: Vol 1   *ISBN: 1 84306 015 9, £22.50*
- Collieries of South Wales: Vol 2   *ISBN: 1 84306 017 5, £19.95*
- Collieries of Somerset & Bristol   *ISBN: 1 84306 029 9, £14.95*
- Copper & Lead Mines around the Manifold Valley, North Staffordshire   *ISBN: 1 901522 77 6, £19.95*
- Images of Cornish Tin   *ISBN: 1 84306 020 5, £29.95*
- Lathkill Dale, Derbyshire, its Mines and Miners   *ISBN: 1 901522 80 6, £8.00*
- Rocks & Scenery the Peak District   *ISBN: 1 84306 026 4, paperback, £7.95*
- Victorian Slate Mining   *ISBN: 1 84306 073 6, £15.95*

Industrial Histories

- Richard Roberts, The Life & Inventions of, 1789 - 1864   *ISBN: 1 84306 027 2, £29.95*
- The Textile Mill Engine   *ISBN: 1 901522 43 1, paperback, £22.50*
- Watt, James, His Life in Scotland, 1736-74   *ISBN 1 84306 045 0, £35.00*
- Wolseley, The Real, Adderley Park Works, 1901-1926   *ISBN 1 84306 052 3, £19.95*

Roads & Transportantion

- Packmen, Carriers & Packhorse Roads   *ISBN: 1 84306 016 7, £19.95*
- Roads & Trackways of Wales   *ISBN: 1 84306 019 1, £22.50*
- Welsh Cattle Drovers   *ISBN: 1 84306 021 3, £22.50*
- Peakland Roads & Trackways   *ISBN: 1 901522 91 1, £19.95*

Regional/Local Histories

- Derbyshire Country Houses: Vol 1   *ISBN: 1 84306 007 8, £19.95*
- Derbyshire Country Houses: Vol 2   *ISBN: 1 84306 041 8, £19.95*
- Lost Houses of Derbyshire   *ISBN: 1 84306 064 7, £19.95*
- Well Dressing   *ISBN: 1 84306 042 6, Full colour, £19.95*
- Crosses of the Peak District   *ISBN 1 84306 044 2, £14.95*
- Shrovetide Football and the Ashbourne Game   *ISBN: 1 84306 063 9, £19.95*
- Historic Hallamshire   *ISBN: 1 84306 049 3, £19.95*
- Colwyn Bay, Its History across the Years   *ISBN: 1 84306 014 0, £24.95*
- Llandudno: Queen of Welsh Resorts   *ISBN 1 84306 048 5, £15.95*
- Llanrwst: the History of a Market Town   *ISBN 1 84306 070 1, £14.95*
- Lost Houses in and around Wrexham   *ISBN 1 84306 057 4, £16.95*
- Shipwrecks of North Wales   *ISBN: 1 84306 005 1, £19.95*